BETTER
CHESS

Part One
IMPROVING YOUR GAME

David Norwood

Edited by Lisa Watts and Carol Varley
Designed by Richard Johnson

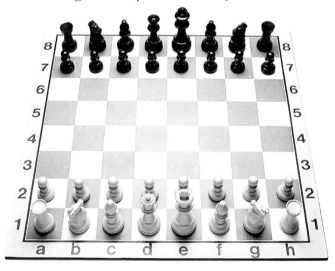

Illustrations by Ian Winter
Photographs by Jane Munro Photography
With thanks to Sheila Jackson

Contents

First published in 1992 by Usborne Publishing Ltd., Usborne House, 83-85 Saffron Hill, London EC1N 8RT, England. © 1992 Usborne Publishing Ltd. The name Usborne and the device ᵂᵂᵂ are Trade Marks of Usborne Publishing Ltd. All rights reserved. No part of this publication may be reproduced, stored in a retrieval system, or transmitted in any form or by any means, electronic, mechanical, photocopying, recording or otherwise, without prior permission of the publisher.
Printed in Portugal.

Using part one

Part one is an introduction to advanced chess techniques. It describes the aims of each stage of the game and alerts you to some of the common pitfalls. All the techniques are clearly explained with example games and moves. It is a good idea to follow the diagrams on a chess board if possible. This will help you to understand the principles that are explained and help you learn how to use them in your own games.

Following the diagrams

The examples are fully illustrated throughout part one, using photographs and move-by-move diagrams. The chess pieces appear as symbols in the diagrams. These are shown on the right. When pieces move, they are shown on the squares they are about to leave. Red or green arrows, like those below right, point to their destination.

All moves are numbered in the diagrams, as on the board below. Chess moves are written in algebraic notation (explained on page 5), and they are highlighted in the text with bold print.

Diagram symbols

King   Queen

Rook   Bishop

Knight   Pawn

Green arrows show where pieces move.

A capture is shown as a red arrow, with a circle around the captured piece.

A hollow red arrow indicates an attack.

A hollow green arrow shows a potential move.

Chess terms

If you discover a chess term that you are unsure of, you can find a clear explanation in the glossary, which starts on page 56.

In the text, words that you may not understand are printed in italics to remind you that they are explained in the glossary.

Tips and tests

There are lists of useful chess tips at the end of most sections to help you remember the essential points which have been covered. Throughout part one there are regular revision puzzles too, so that you can put your new skills to the test. Answers to these puzzles are on pages 61-63.

Assessing your aims

A game of chess can usually be divided into three stages – the *opening*, the *middlegame* and the *endgame*. To improve your game you need to understand the aims and strategies of each stage.

The main features of the opening, the middlegame and endgame are described below, and you can discover more about all three later in part one. In this book, chess moves are written in *algebraic notation*. This is explained on the opposite page.

The opening

In the opening, the players develop their pieces to strong positions in preparation for the middlegame. Rooks and Bishops need to be brought from their starting positions so that they can attack. Pawns are positioned so that they control the centre of the board and the King must be kept safe near the edge of the board.

The middlegame

During the middlegame, players try to weaken each other by attacking their opponent's Pawns and capturing enemy pieces. It is important to make sure that any *exchanges* are to your advantage in the long term, so planning is vital. Your own King must be guarded and you should look for chances to attack the enemy King. The game may end at this stage if a King is exposed.

The endgame

In the endgame, players may have only a few pieces left so these need to be used very carefully. With fewer pieces to attack it, the King is less vulnerable and can join in the action. Pawns become more important and *promoting a Pawn* can become a major aim. Depending on which pieces are left on the board, and how well they are used, the game can end in a win or a draw.

Algebraic notation

Algebraic notation records moves using letters, numbers and symbols. The *ranks* on the board are numbered and the *files* are lettered. Each piece is referred to by its initial, except for the Knight which is N and Pawns for which no initial is used.

A move is written using the initial of the piece and the grid reference of the square it moves to. For example, **Nh3** means the Knight moves to square h3, and **Be3** means the Bishop moves to e3. For a Pawn, only the grid reference of its new position is given. For example, **f4** means a Pawn moves to f4.

Sometimes it is not clear which piece moves so in this case both the initial and file letter of the piece are given. For example, the move **Ne6** could be made by either of the Knights on this board. **Nce6** indicates that the move is made by the Knight on the c-file.

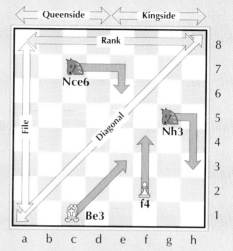

The moves are numbered and White's move is always written first. If Black's move is written without White's, dots are printed after the move number, for example, **4...Ng6**.

Symbols used in notation

Symbol	Example	
x	**Bxh8**	Bishop captures the piece on h8.*
+	**Re7+**	Rook moves to e7 and puts the King in check.
++	**Re7++**	Rook moves to e7 and checkmates the King.
0-0		Castles Kingside (files e-h).
0-0-0		Castles Queenside (files a-d).
!	**Re3!**	Rook makes a good move to e3.
?	**Nf6?**	Knight makes a bad move to f6.
=		The position is equal – neither side has the advantage.
(Q)	**a8(Q)**	White Pawn reaches the eighth rank and is promoted to a Queen.
(N)	**d1(N)**	Black Pawn promotes to a Knight.

0-0 Castles Kingside

0-0-0 Castles Queenside

* When a Pawn captures, only its file letter is given. For example, **bxc5** means that the Pawn on the b-file captures the piece on square c5.

Piece control

One of the best ways to improve your play is by developing a really good understanding of how each piece operates, its strengths and weaknesses, and what it can contribute at each stage of the game.

The next few pages give lots of useful information about how best to use your pieces.

The Bishop

Each player starts with a white-squared Bishop and a black-squared Bishop. Because they move only diagonally, they stay on these colours throughout the game. They can be powerful attacking pieces when they are not blocked in, so it is a good idea to bring them out early. This board shows how a Bishop can control the longest diagonal in two moves: **1. g3; 2. Bg2**, known as *fianchetto*. Notice how the Bishop is aimed like a cannon, protected on three sides by Pawns.

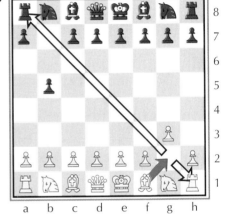

Strong Bishops

It is an advantage to keep both your Bishops (sometimes called the Bishop pair) until you are well into the game. Two Bishops working together control so many squares that they can dominate the board.

It is also important to avoid trapping your Bishops behind Pawns that have become *fixed* in their positions. It is therefore a good idea to bear your Bishops in mind when planning Pawn moves.

Here, White's Bishops and Pawns are working as a team to control a large area of the board. The central Pawns are already fixed but White's Pawns are on black squares so they do not hinder the mobility of the white-squared Bishop. The white-squared Bishop controls the f1-a6 and b1-h7 diagonals, while the black-squared Pawns control squares c5, d6 and f6. A Bishop that works with its Pawns like this is called a *good-squared Bishop*. A Bishop that is trapped by its own Pawns and so has little mobility is called a *bad-squared Bishop*.

The Knight

Knights are the only pieces that can jump over other pieces, so you can bring them out early in the game. They are most powerful near the centre of the board, from where they can move to any of eight squares. A Knight at the side of the board can move to only four squares.

Because they can jump, Knights work well in blocked positions as they can manoeuvre to critical squares and stage surprise attacks. They are at their weakest in the endgame when their slow movement is a hindrance.

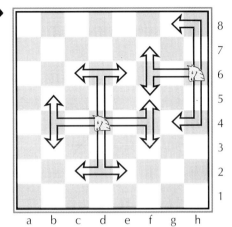

The Rook

Rooks work best on *open files* so, in the opening, you should move them to the centre, where usually you will have created open files with Pawn moves. Castling is one way to do this. Here, White's Rook controls the centre and puts the Black King in check in two moves: **1. 0-0; 2. Re1+**.

Two Rooks on the same rank or file – known as *double Rooks* – are strong as they support each other. They are especially strong on open files where they are not blocked in by Pawns (below left). They have extra power on the seventh rank as they can take pieces left on that rank (below right), or trap the enemy King on the back rank.

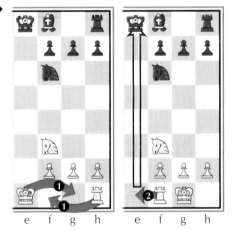

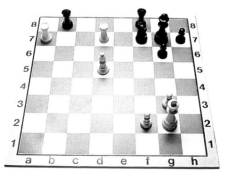

The Queen

The Queen is the most powerful piece on the board as it can move as many squares as you want in a straight line or diagonally. It is a dangerous and effective attacking piece, particularly if enemy pieces are badly co-ordinated or the King is exposed, as on this board. Here, the Queen moves to h4, attacking both the Black King and Rook.

It is best not to develop the Queen too early in the game, though, as it may well be attacked and forced to retreat. Because the Queen is so strong it must always avoid capture.

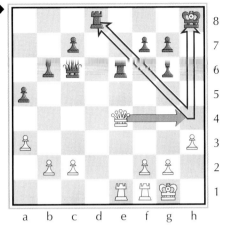

The King

Since the aim of chess is to capture the enemy King, you must keep your King safe at all times. During the opening it is best to move the King to the side by castling. If the King is left in the centre it becomes exposed to attack as the rest of the pieces are developed.

Here, the White King is well defended, protected by a wall of Pawns and a Knight on f3. Black's King is exposed, prevented from castling by the attacking Bishop on a3. (Remember, when castling, your King must not pass over any square that is attacked by your opponent.)

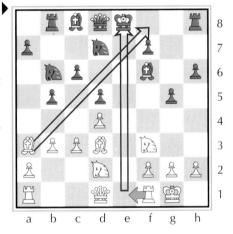

The King is strongest in the endgame when there are only a few pieces left and it can help checkmate the opponent or win pieces. On this board, the Black King is in a good position to win Pawns.

The King can move only one square at a time, so it has no attacking power during the early part of the game. If it is threatened you must immediately make a move to save it.

Piece values and exchanges

Each piece, except for the King, is given a value according to how powerful it is. The King has no value because when it is captured the game is over. It is useful to bear these values in mind when deciding whether it is worth losing a piece in order to capture an enemy piece.

Values

9 points

5 points

3 points

3 points

1 point

Exchanges

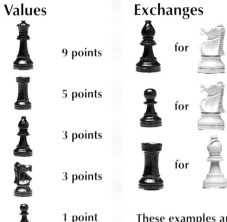

for

If you lose a piece of the same value as the piece you capture, it is a *fair exchange*.

for

If you lose a piece of less value than the piece you capture, you have the *exchange advantage*.

for

If you lose a piece of more value than the piece you capture, you have made a *sacrifice*.

These examples are from Black's point of view.

The piece values are a useful guide but you also have to bear in mind other factors. For example, in the exchange below (**1. Bxe7, Qxe7**), White captures Black's *good-squared Bishop* and loses the weaker of the two White Bishops. Although each side loses a Bishop, Black's Bishop was more mobile and therefore had more value. So in this case, White has the exchange advantage.

Similarly, a Pawn on the seventh rank, which is about to be *promoted*, is worth more than one point.

1. Black has a King and Bishop and White has a King and Knight. Which side is stronger?*

2. Black can move a Knight in order to gain strength. Which Knight should be moved and where to?*

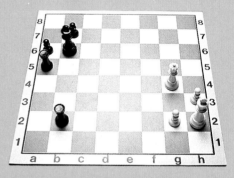

3. Black to play. What would be the best move for the Black Queen?*

4. White to play. How can White win a Rook by moving the Queen?*

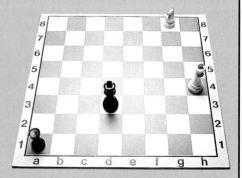

5. White can use the Bishop to capture the Black Knight. How?*

6. How can Black win the Knight and so leave White unable to win?*

Pawns

At the start of the game a Pawn is a minor piece but it can become the strongest piece if it reaches the other end of the board and is *promoted*.* So it is important to move your Pawns with care.

This page shows how the Pawn's role changes during the game. Over the page there are examples of strong *Pawn structures* to aim for and some weak positions to be avoided.

The Pawn's role

During the opening, the Pawns usually defend the centre of the board and play a fairly static role.

In this example, the White Pawns have claimed the centre and form a strong barricade. Notice how squares c5, d5, e5 and f5 are all inaccessible to Black's pieces.

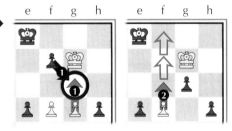

In the middlegame, when development is complete, the Pawns become more active. Their role now is to drive off attacks from enemy pieces and move forward or sacrifice themselves to open attack lines for the Queen, Rooks and Bishops.

Here, White can sacrifice a Pawn and deliver check in two moves: **1.d6!, Qxd6; 2. Bxf7+**. White gives up the Pawn to open the diagonal for the Bishop. White then moves the Bishop up the diagonal to put the Black King in check.

In the endgame, when few pieces are left on the board, Pawns can help the King to win material or to checkmate.

Here, Black has the material advantage; that is, Black's pieces add up to more points than White's in terms of piece value. However, White can gain strength by using the Pawns cleverly: **1. g6! fxg6; 2. f6**. White sacrifices the g-Pawn, and the f-Pawn then advances. Black can now do nothing to stop White's Pawn from reaching the eighth rank and promoting.

* *Although a Pawn is usually made into a Queen when it reaches the eighth rank, it can be promoted to any piece you choose.*

11

Strong Pawn positions

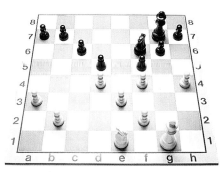

Pawns that are in a group can support each other. Here, Black's Pawns are in fewer groups, or *Pawn islands*, so they are stronger than White's.

Passed Pawns are very strong as they can reach the other end of the board without meeting enemy Pawns on their own or adjacent files.

Here, the Black King is too far away to stop White's a5 Pawn from reaching a8 and promoting. Beware though – enemy territory can be dangerous so your Pawns should usually be supported by other pieces.

In this example, White's Queenside Pawns are connected in a *Pawn chain*. To attack this chain, Black would have to attack the base Pawn on a2.

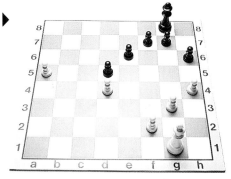

On this board, White's d-Pawn and e-Pawn have formed a central stronghold. By supporting each other they control more squares than they could if they worked independently.

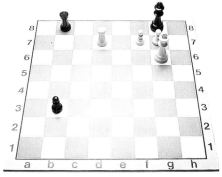

A Pawn on the seventh rank is very strong. Here, the advancing White Pawns have pushed the Black King to the back rank. White has just moved to f7, delivering checkmate.

Weak Pawns

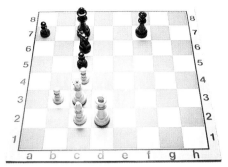

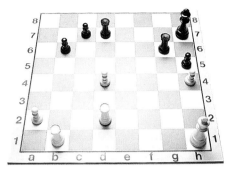

White's b3 Pawn is a *backward Pawn*. It has trailed behind and been left unsupported. If it advances, it will be captured by Black's c5 Pawn.

Here, White has three *isolated Pawns* – they cannot be defended by other Pawns. By playing **1...Rg4**, Black would be sure to win one of these.

◀ On this board, White's *double Pawns* on the b-file are weak. The back Pawn cannot advance until the front Pawn moves and the two Pawns cannot protect each other.

Black's *triple Pawns* are even worse. This time two Pawns must wait for the first Pawn to advance before they can move forward. Avoid trapping Pawns in this way.

Here, White's centre Pawns are *fixed*. The White e-Pawn is blocked by Black's e-Pawn and the Black Knight is preventing the White d-Pawn from moving up the board.

White's *hanging Pawns* on c4 and d4 are relying on *major pieces* rather than Pawns for protection. They have advanced without adequate support and are an easy target for Black.

The opening

During the first few moves of the game you should try to develop your pieces to good positions from which they can attack your opponent in the middlegame. The board below shows some of the better positions for the various pieces, and those to be avoided. The key opposite explains more about the positions shown.

On the next few pages, some famous opening strategies are described. These are series of moves which have been played and analysed for many years. They are named after chess players, or the tournaments at which they became famous.

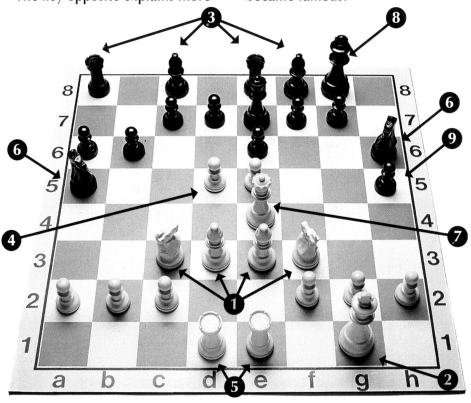

On this board Black has made many mistakes. The Black pieces have no control of the centre and are placed at the sides of the board where they have limited power. Also, Black has taken no care to protect the King. In contrast, White has good piece development and a strong position.

It is important to bring your Rooks, Knights and Bishops into action as quickly as possible. Make sure that you do not begin to attack until you have done this. As a general rule, you should not move any piece more than once until you have finished your development.

Key to board

This key explains the good and bad positions on the board opposite. You can use this as a checklist or guide when you play your openings. If you follow these principles during the early moves of your game, you will handle the opening well and be fully prepared for the middlegame.

1 Develop Knights and Bishops towards the centre.

2 Castle early to keep the King safe.

3 Avoid hemmed-in Bishops and Rooks.

4 Aim to control the centre: put Pawns on d4 and e4 or d5 and e5. If you cannot do this, try to prevent your opponent from dominating the centre.

5 Place Rooks on *open files*, or those least blocked by Pawns.

6 Keep Knights away from the edge of the board.

7 Position your Queen for attack – but not too early as it may be attacked.

8 Do not leave your King exposed to attack – avoid moving the Pawns in front of your King too early as this may leave the King vulnerable.

9 Do not waste time on weak Pawn moves.

Famous openings

Famous openings can be divided into those for White, which try to retain the opening *initiative*, and those for Black, which aim to steal the initiative from White.

Because you can only guess your opponent's responses, famous openings are very flexible. Usually just one or two key moves give an opening its identity.

Some famous openings involve unusual development and moves that contradict the basic opening principles. Because of this, it is unwise to try to play out famous openings in your own game until you are completely sure of all the basic opening rules. Instead, study the mechanics of the openings to see how certain moves put pressure on the opponent and how particular attacks trigger certain replies.

By studying famous openings you can also see how the plans and action of the middlegame are shaped by decisions taken early in the game.

DID YOU KNOW?
- After each side has played three moves, the pieces could form any one of over nine million possible positions on the board. If these were photographed at a rate of one a minute, it would take over 17 years, day and night, to record all the positions.

- The total number of possible games lasting 40 moves each is greater than the number of atoms in the universe.

- The longest game theoretically possible is 5,949 moves.

The Spanish Opening

This popular opening is characterized by White's third move (3. Bb5). Black aims to neutralize White's opening *initiative* before adopting aggressive plans.

1. e4, e5; 2. Nf3, Nc6. Each side advances a Pawn towards the centre. The White Knight then attacks the Black e-Pawn and Black defends it.

3. Bb5, a6. The White Bishop attacks the Black Knight that is defending Black's e-Pawn. Black then attacks the Bishop with a Pawn.

4. Bxc6, dxc6. White captures the Knight and Black takes the Bishop (a *fair exchange*). Black's Queen now has a *semi-open file* along which to attack but the Pawns are *doubled* – a weak position.

5. 0-0, Bd6. The White King castles and Black develops a Bishop to defend the e-Pawn.

6. d4, exd4; 7. Qxd4, f6. White brings out a Pawn to control the centre and Black captures it. The White Queen then captures the Black Pawn and Black moves a Pawn to f6 in order to block the Queen, which is now attacking g7.

8. b3! Be6. White moves the b-Pawn in preparation for *fianchetto*, and Black tries to complete development.

How each side stands

At the end of this opening, Black is still responding to White's moves, so White has retained the initiative. White has a slight positional advantage as the White pieces are slightly better placed than the Black. The White King has castled to safety and White has a Pawn in the centre of the board, as well as a *good-squared Bishop*, which occupies the opposite colour square to most of the Pawns. Also, the White Queen is dominating the centre of the board, backed up by the Rook on f1, which is ready to move to the *open* d-file.

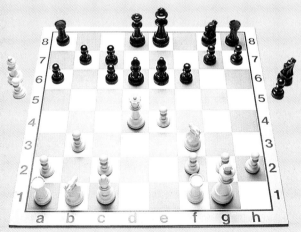

Black, on the other hand, has not yet castled, has weak doubled Pawns on the c-file and a hemmed-in Queen.

However, Black still has both Bishops and the Pawn majority on the Queenside, which could be an advantage.

The King's Gambit

This is an opening for White. Although it begins in the same way as the Spanish Opening, White's second move – the gambit of the King's Bishop's Pawn (the f-Pawn) – gives this opening a character of its own.

A *gambit* is a strategy in which a piece is offered for sacrifice in order to gain advantage later in the game. In this opening, White sacrifices the f-Pawn to open up the f-file. White's moves are aggressive and it is difficult for Black to defend against them.

1. e4, e5; 2. f4, exf4. Both players advance a Pawn. White then offers the f-Pawn for sacrifice and Black captures it, accepting the gambit.

3. Nf3, Be7. White brings out a Knight to prevent the Black Queen from giving check from h4. Black then develops a Bishop.

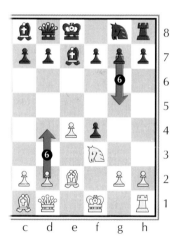

4. Be2! Bh4+. White prepares to castle, but Black prevents this by advancing the Bishop to h4 and putting the White King in check.

5. Kf1, Be7. White moves the King out of check and Black moves the Bishop from h4, where it was a target for the White Knight.

6. d4, g5. White claims the centre and attacks the f4 Pawn with a Bishop. Black defends f4 by advancing the g-Pawn to form a *Pawn chain*.

	d	e	f	g	h

7. h4, g4. White attacks the base of the Pawn chain and Black advances the g-Pawn to attack White's Knight.

8. Ne5, h5. White brings out a Knight to attack Black's weak Pawns on f7 and g4. Black defends the g-Pawn.

9. Bc4, Rh7. White moves a Bishop to c4, from where it attacks the Pawn on f7. Black advances a Rook to defend f7.

How each side stands

After playing **10. Bxf4**, White controls the centre and has good piece development, as shown here. White also has space in which to manoeuvre and chances to attack the Black King.

Black has no central control and has barely begun piece development. However, Black can now play **10...d6**, attacking the Knight and opening the diagonal for the c8 Bishop.

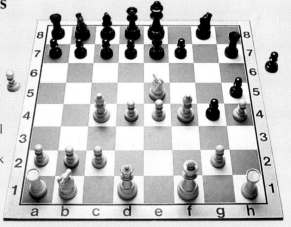

A trick for Black

It is interesting to consider how Black could have changed the outcome of this opening with an early move. If possible, follow these moves on a chess board.

1. e4, e5; **2. f4, Bc5**. Black offers the e-Pawn as a *counter gambit*. If White accepts with **3.fxe5**, White will lose by the following sequence: **3...Qh4+**; **4.Ke2, Qxe4++**.

The Caro-Kann

This is an opening for Black that can be used in response to 1. e4. It is named after two famous 19th century players, H. Caro and M. Kann.

In this opening, Black challenges the centre in an unusual way and pays less attention to piece development. Black's plan is to establish a strong defence with a solid Pawn structure before beginning to attack. Black's first two moves give this opening its identity.

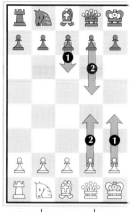

1. e4, c6; 2. d4, d5. Black allows White to take the centre and then issues a direct challenge to White's e-Pawn.

3. e5, Bf5. White does not *exchange* central Pawns but pushes the e-Pawn forward. Black develops the weaker of the two Bishops.

4. Bd3, Bxd3; 5. Qxd3, e6. In these two moves White's strongest Bishop is exchanged for Black's weaker Bishop. White should have avoided this exchange as it has given Black control of the white squares. Instead, White could have moved the Bishop to e2, or advanced the Kingside Pawns to g4, h4 and so on.

6. Nc3, Qb6. White develops a Knight, but Black, who has adopted an unusual plan, neglects normal development and brings out the Queen.

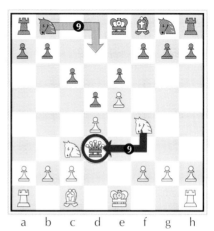

7. Nge2, Qa6; **8. Nf4, Qxd3**. White continues with development and Black prepares to exchange Queens. White allows the exchange of Queens but this is an error since Black has the *positional advantage*, with a more mobile Bishop and strong Pawns.

9. Nxd3, Nd7=. Black *equalizes*. White no longer has the opening *initiative* and the *material* is level – both sides have the same pieces. Also, the strengths and weaknesses of each side are evenly matched, as explained below.

How each side stands

At this stage, with an even balance between the two sides, both players need to exploit their strengths in order to gain the advantage. In the long term, Black has more chance to control the centre by moving Pawns to c5 and f6. These Pawn moves must be carefully prepared and used when they will have most impact.

White, on the other hand, has slightly better development, although this is less significant after the exchange of

Queens. With no Queens on the board the Kings no longer need such tight

protection as their most threatening attackers are gone.

The King's Indian Defence

The key feature of this opening for Black is the immediate *fianchetto* of Black's King's Bishop. In the early moves, Black purposely allows White's Pawns to control the centre. Black then plots to undermine them, using the fianchettoed Bishop as a weapon.

1. d4, Nf6. White advances a central Pawn and Black develops a Knight, preventing White from taking the centre immediately with a Pawn move to e4.

2. c4, g6. White continues to aim for the centre by advancing the c-Pawn and Black pushes forward the g-Pawn in preparation for fianchetto.

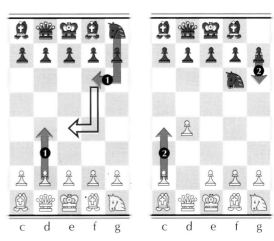

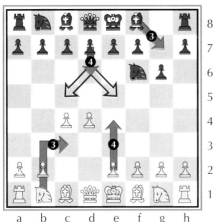

3. Nc3, Bg7; 4. e4, d6. After first moving the Knight as defence, White moves the e-Pawn. Black completes fianchetto, and advances the d-Pawn. Black's Pawn move is important as it frees the c8 Bishop, prevents White from moving a Pawn to e5 and prepares for a central challenge.

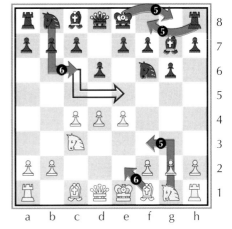

5. Nf3, 0-0; 6. Be2, Nc6. White develops a Knight and Black castles. White then continues with normal development and Black advances the Knight. Black is getting ready to challenge White's control of the centre by bringing a Pawn to e5; the Knight will give support.

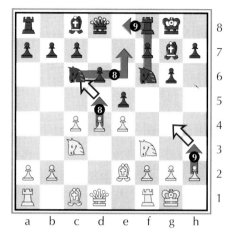

7. 0-0, e5. White castles and Black brings forward the e-Pawn as planned, threatening White's *Pawn centre*. White could have avoided this challenge by pushing the d-Pawn forward to d5. However, this move would have been risky: if Black's f6 Knight moved, the a1-h8 diagonal would be left open for the fianchettoed Bishop.

8. d5, Ne7. White advances the d-Pawn to block the centre as the dangerous fianchettoed Bishop is now obstructed on both e5 and f6. The Black Knight then retreats.

9. h3, Ne8! White advances the h-Pawn to prevent Black from playing **9...Ng4.** This move would clear the way for a Pawn advance to f5. Instead the Black Knight backs off to e8.

How each side stands

At this point Black's plan is working well. Next, Black will play **10...f5.** If White captures the f-Pawn with **11. exf5**, Black can reply with **11...gxf5.** Black will then control the central squares and the powerful fianchettoed Bishop will be free again. Black is also ready to advance Pawns down the Kingside.

All is not lost for White, though. White has more manoeuvring space than Black and can still gain the

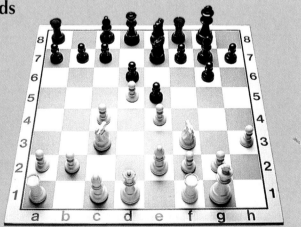

overall advantage by defending well on the

Kingside and advancing the Queenside Pawns.

The middlegame

When both sides have protected the King and developed their pieces to positions from which they can attack or defend, the middlegame begins. Both players become more aggressive as they try to weaken one another's position and gain the advantage.

In the middlegame it is important to assess your own position on the board, identify your opponent's weakest points and form a strategy to exploit them.* The example strategies on the next few pages show some ways in which you might do this.

Middlegame example 1

On this middlegame board, White has the better development. White's Rooks dominate the central files and White also has more space in which to manoeuvre. At this point, each side has lost a Bishop and a Pawn.

It is White's turn. White plans to open up the b1-h7 diagonal so that the White Queen can attack the Black King, or the Knight on d7.

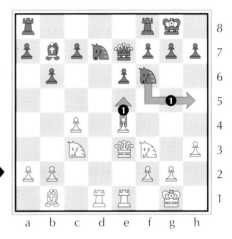

1. e5, Nh5. White moves the e-Pawn to open up the diagonal and forces Black to move the Knight on f6 out of the line of attack. This Knight was crucial to Black's defence as it protected the Knight on d7 and the Pawn on h7.

A piece which is relied on too heavily for defence, like the Knight in this example, is said to be *overloaded*.

2. Qd3, g6; **3. Qxd7**. First, White moves the Queen to d3, threatening checkmate with **3. Qxh7** and attacking the unprotected Knight on d7. Black advances the g-Pawn, creating an escape square for the vulnerable King. White then captures the Knight, leaving Black with a *material disadvantage* and grave prospects. Through careful planning, White is now in a strong position.

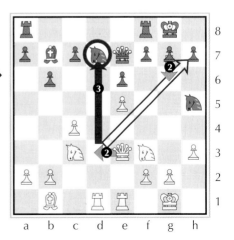

You can learn more about planning on pages 35-39.

Middlegame example 2

On this board White has the *material advantage* but Black's pieces are very well placed. Black plans to achieve a winning position by opening up the h-file. It is Black's turn to move.

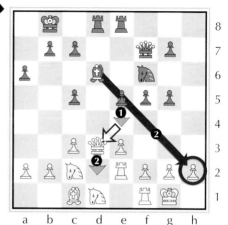

1...e4; 2. Qd2, Bxh2+. Black's first Pawn move opens the diagonal for the Bishop and threatens the White Queen. White then moves the Queen out of danger and Black captures the Pawn on h2 – putting the White King in check and opening the h-file for Black's Rooks, Queen and Knight.

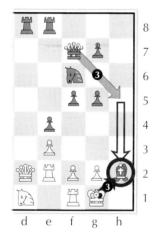

◀ **3. Kxh2, Qh5+.** The White King captures its attacker but is put in check again by Black's Queen, which moves to the open h-file.

4. Kg1, Ng4. The White King retreats. Black could have captured White's Queen with **4...Rxd2** but instead prepares for an attack on a greater prize – the White King.

5. Qxd8, Rxd8. Faced with imminent checkmate (**5...Qh2++**). White can only stall for time. By taking the Black Rook, however, White merely loses the Queen.

6. Rfe1, Qh2+. White moves a Rook to create a temporary retreat for the King and so avoid immediate checkmate. The Black Queen moves to give check from h2.

7.Kf1, Qh1++. The doomed White King backs away but is immediately checkmated by the Black Queen.

Middlegame example 3

Here, White has some power over the centre, with the Rook controlling the open e-file. The Black King has castled and is safe but the Black Knight is badly positioned. White's best plan is to break up the Black Kingside Pawns and penetrate Black's defences with the Queen and Rook.

1. Bxf6, gxf6. White's Bishop takes the Black Knight and Black captures White's Bishop with a Pawn. This is a *fair exchange* but White has drawn a Pawn from the Black King's defences.

2. Re3!, Rfe8. White moves a Rook to e3 – a good move as, from this square, the Rook can cross to the h-file, or dominate the e-file. Black, forced to act defensively, moves a Rook to challenge the e-file.

White's next two moves are **3. Rh3** and **4. Qh5** – bringing two powerful pieces to back each other up along the h-file. Regardless of Black's response, White will, at least, win the h-Pawn and seriously weaken Black's defences.

Middlegame example 4

In this example, Black's plan is to play for central control by capturing White's *good-squared Bishop*. It is Black's turn to move.

1...Nxd3. Black takes the Bishop with a Knight. **2. Qxd3, Nd5.** Black then loses the Knight to the Queen (a fair exchange). Black's f6 Knight leaps to d5, from where it can control the centre as White has no c-Pawn or e-Pawn to chase it.

In two moves Black has weakened White's position and gained power.

Middlegame example 5

In this example, White's plan is to open the h-file and focus the attack on the Kingside.

1. h4, Qa5. White advances a Pawn up the h-file and Black mobilizes the Queen. Black cannot block the White Pawn with **1...h5** because the Black Pawn would be taken with **2. gxh5**, opening up the h-file. Black is also prevented from moving the Knight on f6 as this Knight is shielding the Black Queen from the g5 Bishop. By moving the Queen, Black releases the f6 Knight and provokes action on the Queenside. White can continue the attack down the h-file with **2. h5**, and **3. Bh6** (to remove Black's defending Bishop on g7), then **4. hxg6**, forcing Black to play

4...hxg6. This exchange of Pawns will open up the h-file and leave Black in a dangerous position.

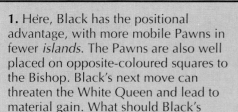

Test yourself

1. Here, Black has the positional advantage, with more mobile Pawns in fewer *islands*. The Pawns are also well placed on opposite-coloured squares to the Bishop. Black's next move can threaten the White Queen and lead to material gain. What should Black's move be?*

2. On this board, White is stronger, with more Pawns in fewer islands. White will probably win the game – one way would be by doubling Rooks on the b-file. First, though, White can capture a Black Bishop. Which one should be captured?*

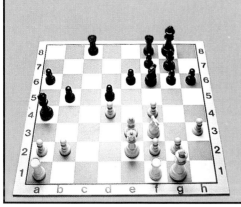

*Puzzle answers on pages 61-63.

The endgame

As more pieces are *exchanged*, the game approaches the endgame. In this phase, opportunities for checkmate usually become fewer, especially if the players have exchanged Queens. Now the King can venture from its defended position to join in the attack, or help to *promote a Pawn* – one of the main aims in the endgame.

Mobilizing the King

Here, both sides need to bring their King into action. Black's outlook is bleak as the King cannot attack any of White's Pawns and the Bishop is powerless. In contrast, White has a *good-squared Bishop*, a strong Pawn structure and can mobilize the King. By advancing diagonally, the White King can attack square a5, allowing the Bishop to capture Black's most vulnerable Pawn. In the middlegame, the threat of checkmate would have made such a King advance impossible.

King and Pawn endgames

When each side has only the King and some Pawns, you need to calculate moves carefully in order to promote a Pawn before your opponent. Here, Black can promote as follows: **1.Kd4, Kg5**; **2.Kc5, Kxg4**; **3. Kxb5, Kxh5**;

4. Kxa4, Kg4. Black's Pawn can now march up the h-file and become a Queen. White is unable to promote the a-Pawn because, by the time it reaches a8, that square will be controlled by Black's new Queen.

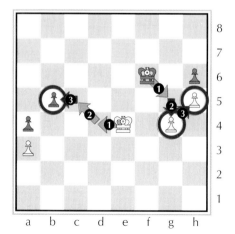

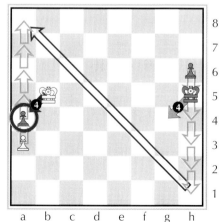

Gaining the opposition

When the two Kings are facing each other along a file, with only one square in between, the player who moved last is said to have the *opposition*. The other King must move back or to the side as an advance would be illegal. You can sometimes make a stalling move, called *losing a tempo*, in order to gain the opposition.

In a King and Pawn endgame you can use the opposition to steer the enemy King away from the *queening square* and so allow your Pawn to promote, as shown in this example.

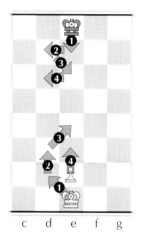  

1. Kd2, Ke7; 2. Kd3, Kd7. (If Black played **2...Ke6**, White's next move would gain the opposition.) **3. Ke4, Ke6.** Now Black has the opposition, but White can regain it by losing a tempo: **4. e3!** Black must now sidestep with **4...Kd6.** The moves continue with **5. Kf5, Ke7.** (If Black played **5...Kd5** then White would play **6. e4+.**)

6. Ke5 (keeping the opposition), **6...Kd7; 7. Kf6** (White must not push the Pawn to e4 yet, as **7...Ke7** would then gain the opposition for Black) **7...Kd6; 8.e4.** Now the White King controls the squares ahead of the Pawn and it can progress in safety. The Black King can now do nothing to stop the Pawn from promoting.

An alternative ending

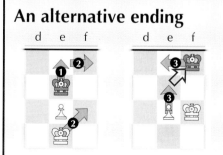

It is vital that the King advances in front of the Pawn. If White had played **1. e4**, the players may have reached the positions shown far left. Black could then draw, with: **1...Ke8!**; **2. Kf6, Kf8; 3. e7+, Ke8.** Black's last move makes it impossible for the White Pawn to promote, so White must abandon it or play **4. Ke6**, leading to· *stalemate*.

Rook endgames

In a Rook endgame, each side has only a Rook, a few Pawns and the King. This is the most common type of endgame.

With only one *major piece* left, apart from the King, you need to use it to the full, so you should try to place your Rook on an *open file* where it will have the greatest influence. Another key to winning Rook and Pawn endgames is to create a *passed Pawn*. Your Rook and Pawns need to work together very carefully to achieve this.

The examples on these two pages outline three techniques that will help you to win Rook and Pawn endgames.

Keeping active

On this board the Black and White Pawn and King positions are symmetrical. Only the places of the Rooks are different – but this is all-important. White's Rook is superbly placed: it is attacking Black's a5, f6 and h5 Pawns.

Black's Rook has no mobility. It has to defend the f6 and h5 Pawns and, if it moves, one of these Pawns will be lost. Also, the Black King must stay on b6 or a6 to defend the a5 Pawn. White's Rook dominates the board; it controls Black's moves and the White King has total freedom.

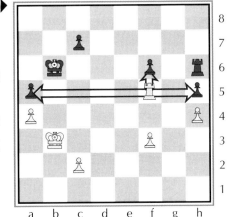

Creating passed Pawns

A passed Pawn has two uses. You can make a direct attempt to *promote* it or you can use it as a decoy: while your opponent is attempting to stop your passed Pawn from promoting, you can capture the Pawns whose defence has been abandoned.

On the board on the right it is Black's turn to move. Black plays **1...Re8** to prevent White from promoting the Pawn on e7. White can now switch plans and capture the f5 and h5 Pawns. White loses the passed Pawn on e7, but now has two connected passed Pawns on f4 and g3.

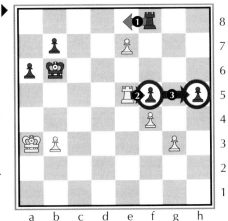

Rooks and passed Pawns

Be careful to keep your Rook behind a passed Pawn or it will block the Pawn's advance, as shown in the example on the right. Here, Black appears to be winning as White's pieces cannot move.* However, the Black Rook is in front of the passed Pawn on a2. By remaining on a1, the Rook stops the Pawn from promoting, but if it moves, White can play **Rxa2**.

Black could only promote by moving the King to b2 or b3 to defend the Pawn so that the Rook can move. Black cannot achieve this though, as the King has no cover and would be constantly checked by White's Rook. So Black has no winning plan.

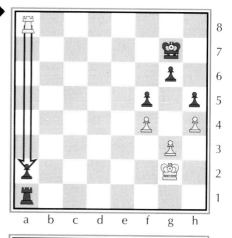

In contrast, on this board the Black Rook is behind the passed Pawn and it is White's Rook that is trapped on a1. Black needs to bring the King to b2 to force the Rook to move and allow the Pawn to promote. White can only prevent this by moving the King to the Queenside, but by doing so, White will abandon the defence of the Kingside Pawns, which can then be mopped up by Black's King. Here, Black is in an excellent position to win pieces.

Endgame tips

Many of the principles of Rook and Pawn endgames also apply to Knight, Bishop and even Queen endgames.

• Use your King. Note that in all the above examples the King plays a vital role in carrying out the plan.

• Remember that in most endgames, the King changes from a piece to be defended to an attacking piece.

• Keep pieces active; combine both attack and defence as best you can.

• Guard your passed Pawns – and try to prevent your opponent from getting a passed Pawn too.

• Be sure you can support passed Pawns without making your pieces passive, as in the first example opposite.

---

* Can you see what would happen if the King or Rook moved? Puzzle answers on pages 61-63.

Winning, drawing or losing

Endgames have been studied by chess analysts for centuries and the outcome of endgames with certain combinations of pieces is well known. It is useful to bear the winning combinations in mind when *exchanging* pieces or going into the endgame. These two pages show some common winning, losing and drawing combinations. In each example, Black is attacking and White defending. There is a chart showing other combinations on page 34.

 against ♔

A King with two Bishops is an easy win against a lone King. Keep your pieces together and corner the King, trapping it in a mating net (see Endgame techniques below). Here, Black plays **1...Be4+**. White must then play **2. Ka1**. Black's next move, **2...Bd4**, is checkmate.

♛ + ♟ + ♞ against ♔

The King, Bishop and Knight can win against the King but it is tricky. On the board below, Black checkmates with **1...Nc1; 2. Ka1, Bd4++**, forcing the King into a corner of the same colour as the Bishop's square. This is called the dangerous corner (see Endgame techniques below).

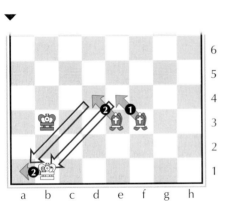

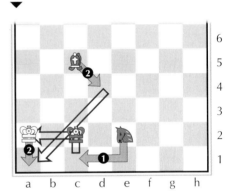

Endgame techniques

In both the examples on this page, you have to form a *mating net* to win. In a mating net your pieces are placed so that wherever the King moves, it is trapped. It is impossible to checkmate the King in the centre of the board when you have only a few pieces, so it is vital that you corner the King.

Note how, in the second example, the attacking Bishop is black-squared

and the King is checkmated in a black corner. This is the dangerous corner. It is impossible to force checkmate in a non-dangerous corner – a corner of the opposite colour to that of your Bishop's square. If the enemy King is aiming for a non-dangerous corner, try to force it across to a dangerous corner so that you can form a mating net and win the game.

An interesting position is shown here. Black has a Bishop and Pawn but, surprisingly, this is not enough to win. This is because the Rook's Pawn (the one that starts on the same file as the Rook) is heading for h1 – a white square which the Bishop cannot control. Black cannot force the White King to move from this corner and the Pawn will not be able to *promote*. This situation is called the Bishop and wrong Rook's Pawn, and is always a draw if the enemy King can reach the vital corner in time.

If the Bishop was on g6, Black would be able to win easily as the Bishop

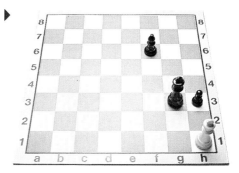

could control h1. In the example shown here the game will end in *stalemate*, for example with:
1. Kg1, Bd4+; **2. Kh1, h2** stalemate.

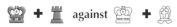
For this combination to result in a draw, the side with the *minor piece* needs to aim for the non-dangerous corner – as White has done here. In this position, Black cannot make progress. White should move the Bishop between a7 and b8. If Black prevents this by moving a Rook to f8, White can move the King to and fro between a8 and a7. Black cannot break this repetitive pattern without forcing stalemate – with **1...Ba7**; **2. Rf8+, Bb8**; **3. Kb6** for example.

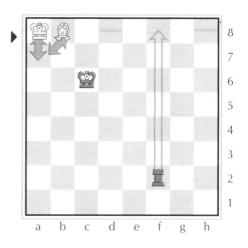

This combination can be a draw as long as the side with the minor piece (White in this example) keeps the King and Knight together.

On this board, although the Knight prevents immediate checkmate from **1...Rd1++**, White is vulnerable as the King and Knight are separated. Black can move **1...Rd2** forcing the Knight to c4 or a4 to avoid capture. Black can then play **2...Rd1++**.

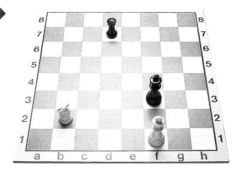

Other winning or drawing combinations

♔ + ♗/♘ against ♚	Draw	It is impossible to construct a mating net with a King and Bishop, or King and Knight.
♔ + ♙ (Rook's Pawn) against ♚	Draw	This is always a draw as long as the defending King can advance in front of the enemy Pawn, preventing it from promoting.
♔ + ♘ + ♘ against ♚	Draw	The Knights cannot force the enemy King into a mating net.
♔ + ♖ against ♚	Win	The King and Rook can force the enemy King to one side and easily give checkmate.
♔ + ♕ against ♚ + ♖	Win	You can use the King and Queen to push the enemy King to the side, then try to *fork* the King and Rook with the Queen.

Test yourself

1. White to play. How can White promote a Pawn and win?*

2. How can White avoid losing this endgame? White to play.*

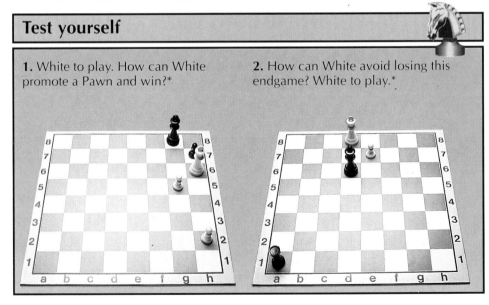

Planning

In order to improve your game you should try to make sure that every one of your moves is part of a plan. The examples on pages 24-27 illustrate the benefits of planning in the middlegame; the examples on the next few pages deal with the art of planning at other stages of the game.

The first stage of any plan is to decide on your aim. Checkmate is rarely a realistic short term goal, but you may be able to *promote a Pawn*, make an *exchange* or improve your defence. Having decided on your objective, the next stage is to find the best way to. achieve it.

Planning example 1

The best way to decide on a plan is to search for weaknesses in your opponent's position. A weak *Pawn structure*, for example, is an excellent target for attack. If, on the other hand, your own Pawns are weak, a more useful objective may be to improve their defence.

Forming the plan

On this endgame board the *material* is level (both sides have the same pieces left) but White has a weak Pawn structure, with isolated Pawns on the Queenside. Black has to decide on a plan which will exploit the weakness in White's Pawn structure and White has to adopt a defensive plan. It is Black's turn to move.

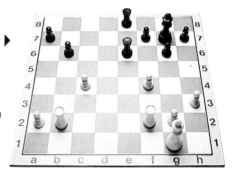

Carrying out the plan

First Black can attack the weak c4 Pawn with **1...Rc8**. White could defend with **2. Rbc2** but this would enable Black to capture the c-Pawn by doubling Rooks on the c-file (**2...Rec6**). So instead White chooses an alternative defensive move – **2. Rb4**. Now, if Black does double the Rooks on the c-file, White can defend by playing **3. Rc2**.

Black now changes plan and plays **2...Re4!** With this move Black will win either the c4 or f4 Pawn – thanks to careful planning.

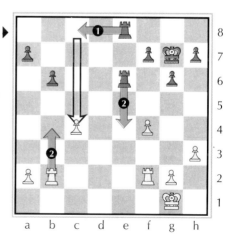

Planning example 2

In the planning example on the previous page, Black's plan involved only a couple of moves to exploit an obvious weakness in White's Pawn structure. Although most games require more sophisticated plans, the attack or defence of Pawn structure is still very often the central objective – as you can see from the model game that follows.

Forming the plan

This board shows the positions of the pieces after the fifth move of a version of the Modern Benoni opening.* Each side has lost a Pawn: White has lost the c-Pawn and taken Black's e-Pawn.

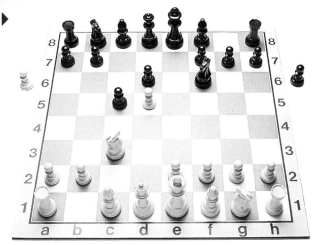

It is early in the game and neither side is in a position to give checkmate or win material. However, there are already several features around which each side can make plans. White has more central Pawns and so will want to build on this strength.

Black, on the other hand, is weak in the centre, having already lost the e-Pawn, but strong on the Queenside. In addition, Black's King's Bishop is blocked in, so Black will probably plan to mobilize this Bishop with a *fianchetto* move.

Carrying out the plan

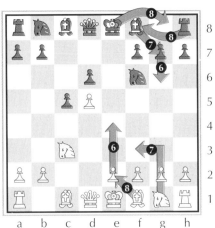

White's next move is **6. e4**, gaining strength in the centre of the board and opening the f1-a6 diagonal to give the Bishop mobility. Black's King's Bishop has little mobility on the a3-f8 diagonal, which is blocked by the Pawns on c5 and d6. Black therefore moves **6...g6** in preparation for fianchetto.

Both sides continue with sensible developing moves as shown on the board on the left:

7. Nf3, Bg7; 8. Be2, 0-0.

Most famous openings have several different versions. An alternative version of this opening appears on page 47.

9. 0-0, Re8. White now castles to move the King from the centre file, and Black brings a Rook to the *semi-open* e-file, threatening the e4 Pawn. Like the fianchetto, this move is determined by the Pawn structure – in this case, the absence of Black's e-Pawn.

Both sides can now concentrate on their main plan: White aims to dominate the centre with Pawn advances to f4 and e5, and Black is planning to advance on the Queenside, and create a *passed Pawn*.

10. Nd2, a6. White moves the Knight to prepare for Pawn expansion in the centre. Black advances a Queenside Pawn as planned. Note how Black's fianchettoed Bishop on g7 is already positioned to support the Pawns as they near their *queening squares*.

Next, Black plans to move **11...b5**, to control squares a4, b4, c4 and d4 and so dominate the Queenside. However, White anticipates this and plays **11. a4!** (Although White wants to expand in the centre, it is more important to stop Black's advance to b5.) Instead, Black plays **11...Nbd7**, gaining control of e5.

Taking stock

Look again at the starting positions to see how the Pawn structure affected each side's plans. White's plan was based on strong central Pawns, and Black's on a Queenside Pawn majority.

Pawn structure also dictated piece development – such as Black's Bishop and Rook advances. Note how Black's c8 Bishop was left undeveloped because White's Pawns left it no active square to move to.

Continuing the plan

Now study the positions on the board after Black's eleventh move. Consider the objective of each side: Black is still planning to advance the b-Pawn to b5 and White, after moving the f-Pawn, intends to push forward the e-Pawn.

Both sides need to support their planned advances as well as possible. What preparations could the players make to help them achieve their objectives?*

Puzzle answers on pages 61-63.

Planning example 3

In the following example, neither side has any immediate targets – the Kings are well defended and the pieces are adequately protected. Again, studying the Pawn structure provides the basis for a plan.

White's Pawn structure is fairly solid but Black has an isolated Queen's Pawn on d5. This Pawn is a weakness. Although it creates space for Black's other pieces, it cannot be defended by Pawns.

Forming the plan

It is White's move. A reasonable long term plan for White is to capture the d-Pawn. Black, however, is trying to advance this Pawn in order to exchange it. It has no useful role, so should be exchanged for White's e-Pawn.

White must construct a plan to take the d-Pawn. *Isolated Pawns* are weaker if they cannot advance, so first White must try to block the d-Pawn. The square in front of an isolated Pawn is a safe outpost for the other side.

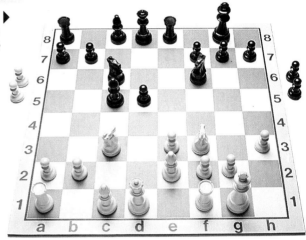

Black has no c-Pawn or e-Pawn and so cannot challenge square d4. White should therefore devise a plan to secure this square, while continuing to develop other pieces.

Carrying out the plan

◀ **1. Nb5! a6**. White's Knight is aiming for d4. The f3 Knight could have moved there immediately but Black would then have played **1...Nxd4**. Then, after **2. exd4** both sides would have a similar Pawn structure and White's plan would be useless. With the next moves, **2. Nd4, Bd7**, White takes square d4 and Black brings out a Bishop. Black has no obvious plan: Black's first two moves were pointless as the White Knight was clearly heading for d4, and the Black Bishop has no function on the a4-e8 diagonal.

3. b3!, Rb8; 4. Bb2. White's Queenside fianchetto mobilizes the Bishop, which was unable to move on the blocked c1-h6 diagonal. On the long a1-h8 diagonal the Bishop can reinforce the blockade on d4. Again, Black's move was pointless – the Rook has no future on a closed file, blocked by its own Pawn. It really belongs on the *open* c-file.

By studying the Pawn structure and planning carefully, White has gained the advantage in just a few moves. Having blockaded the d5 Pawn, White can now consider plans to attack it.

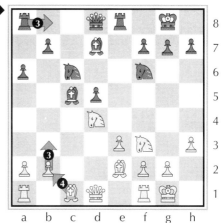

Test yourself

1. Consider the positions after White's fourth move in the above example. The next stage of White's plan is to capture the d-Pawn, so White has to prepare for this. What are the best positions for the White Rooks in order to help with this plan?*

2. It is White's move. What plan should White adopt and why? Remember, identify Black's weakness, then work out a plan to exploit it.*

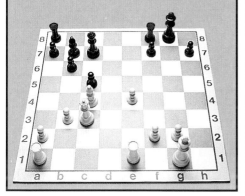

Planning tips

• Look for easy targets such as an exposed King, undefended pieces, *double Pawns* or isolated Pawns, and find ways to exploit them.

• Look at your own position and rectify any glaring weaknesses.

• If there are no easy targets and your position is fairly sound, look for opportunities to create *passed Pawns*, and consider possible sacrifices and tactics.**

• If none of the above is feasible, consider long term plans. Study the Pawn structure to work out the best positions for your pieces.

• Be alert to your opponent's moves and try to guess the plan behind them. Find ways to foil your opponent's plan whilst pursuing your own.

• Do not be afraid to switch plans if necessary. Keep flexible and do not embark on a long and difficult plan if you are not sure it will work.

* Puzzle answers on pages 61-63.
** See pages 42-45.

39

Defence

Throughout the game, all of your pieces should be working together to defend and support each other, but the most important piece to defend is, of course, the King.

In most cases, King defence is straightforward: you need to make sure that it never becomes exposed along files or diagonals and, if enemy pieces begin to crowd in on your King, you should fend them off. There are certain situations, though, when an apparently well-defended King can be the victim of a mating attack. Some of these are described here.

Back rank mate

◀ Here, Black has the *material advantage* and the Black King is barricaded by a wall of Pawns. However, White can force checkmate. Follow the moves to see how this is possible.

Notice how Black is forced into checkmate on the eighth rank (known as *back rank mate*). This occurs because the Pawns that are defending the Black King are also trapping it on the back rank. You can guard against back rank mate by moving the h-Pawn one square to give the King a retreat – as White has done here.

1. Qxd8

1...Rxd8; 2. Re8+

2...Rxe8

3. Rxe8++

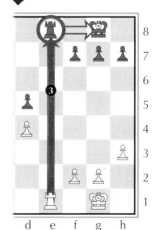

40

Exchanging the fianchettoed Bishop

If you *fianchetto* your Bishop so that it sits in front of your King, avoid *exchanging* it, except for the Bishop that occupies the same colour square. If you trade it for the Bishop on the opposite colour square, your opponent has control of the critical diagonal in front of your King.

Here, White has exchanged the white-squared fianchettoed Bishop on g2 for Black's black-squared Bishop. The h1-a8 diagonal is now completely controlled by Black's Queen and white-squared Bishop. Black can now give checkmate on g2 or h1.

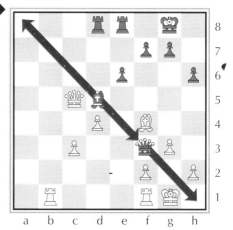

Defence tips

- See if you can divert an attack on your own pieces by attacking your opponent's King or other pieces.

- Do not give your opponent *open files* or diagonals that lead to your King.

- Do not let your opponent bring a lot of pieces close to your King.

- If under heavy attack, exchanging Queens, as described below, may ease the situation.

- Look after the fianchetto Bishop as described above.

- To avoid a back rank mate, provide your King with an escape square.

Exchanging Queens

Here Black is under heavy attack – the Black King is exposed and threatened with **1. Rh7+**. Without swift defensive action Black will either be checkmated or lose the Queen. In this situation, Black's best means of defence is to play **1...Qe5+**, forcing the exchange of Queens – **2. Qxe5, dxe5**.

Now, if White plays **3. Rh7+**, the Black King can simply advance, with **3...Ke6**. The Black King is able to support the advance of the e-Pawn and f-Pawn and can also help capture White's f-Pawn.

Tactical combinations

You need to be constantly on the lookout for ways to gain the advantage over your opponent. To succeed, you often need to use tactical combinations. These are series of moves that force your opponent to make certain replies. The aim may be *material* gain, *promoting a Pawn*, a better position or perhaps checkmate.

Tactical combinations often involve the use of *sacrifices* and devices such as *pins, forks, skewers* and *discovered attacks*. Be wary if a piece of yours is caught in one of these attacks and look very closely to see what your opponent is trying to do. It is possible that you are about to become the victim of a tactical combination which could lead to your downfall.

Combination 1

On the board on the right, it is White's ▶ turn to move. White has fewer pieces but can use a tactical trick to win material.

By playing **1. Bc7**, White reveals a *discovered check* by the White Rook. By moving to c7 White's Bishop does the maximum amount of damage to Black as, from this position, it attacks the Black Queen. Black is forced to move the King out of check first, so cannot avoid losing the Queen with White's next move.

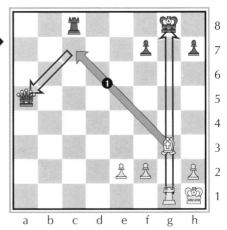

Combination 2

Although this combination is only two ◀ moves long, it features a pin, a sacrifice and a Knight fork.

White plays **1. d3** to free the c1 Bishop. However, this move also opens the diagonal on which both the White King and Queen are aligned – so this is a perfect place for Black to deal a tactical blow.

Black plays **1...Bb4!**, pinning the Queen. The Bishop is undefended, but Black has planned a combination which will sacrifice this Bishop in order to trap the Queen in a Knight fork, as described at the bottom of the opposite page.

Combination 3

Here, White uses a pin to force a series of moves and win material. Black played **1...Bg4** last move. Although this attacked White's Queen, it was a blunder. The only piece defending the Black Bishop is the Knight on f6 – and this piece is pinned to the Queen. If the Knight moves, the Queen is exposed to attack by the White Bishop. White can exploit this pin, as shown below.

White can play **2. Bxf6!** If Black then captures the Bishop on f6 with **2...Qxf6**, White can play **3. Qxg4**, winning a piece.

If, on the other hand, Black replies to **2. Bxf6!** by moving **2...Bxd1**, White can play **3. Bxd8** and the two sides exchange Queens.

Now, if Black's next move is **3...Bxc2**, capturing a Pawn, White can mirror the move with **4. Bxc7** and so remain one piece ahead.

---

2. Qxb4. White has to accept the sacrifice or Black will play **3...Bxc3+**. This forces White's Queen to square b4 – the ideal position for a Knight fork from c2. Black plays **2...Nxc2+**, bringing the Knight to c2, from where it forks the Queen and King. The King must move, so Black takes the Queen.

As this example shows, you should never leave both your King and Queen on an open diagonal that can be controlled by the enemy Bishop.

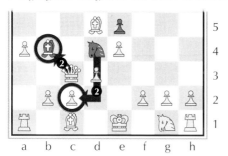

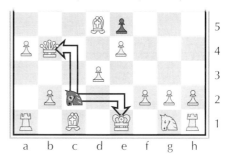

More tactical combinations

Tactical moves frequently centre around hot-spots on the board such as the King, or a Pawn that is close to *promoting* – as in the examples on these two pages.

Combination 4

On this board, White's last move was **Bc4**, pinning the Queen to the King. However, this tactical blow from White fails to a more subtle tactical combination from Black, which sacrifices the Queen to achieve *back rank mate*. Black plays **1...Qxc4!** offering up the Queen.

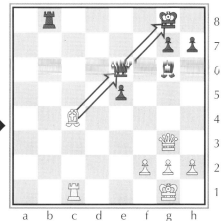

White has to take the Queen (**2. Rxc4**) to prevent Black from playing **2...Qxc1+**. Black can now continue with the next stage of the combination by playing **2...Rb1+**.

White's only way to get the King out of check is to play **3. Rc1**, to block the path of the Black Rook. Black can now remove the White Rook with **3...Rxc1++** and checkmate the King, as shown below.

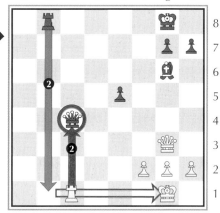

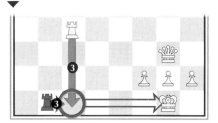

Notice how, in the final position, White's Pawns trap the White King instead of protecting it. Remember, to avoid this situation it is a good idea to play a move such as **h3** early in the game, giving your King an escape square.

Tactical tips

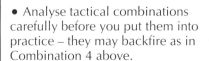

- Analyse tactical combinations carefully before you put them into practice – they may backfire as in Combination 4 above.

- Before using a tactical combination involving a *sacrifice*, make certain that you will not lose more *material* than you gain.

Combination 5

Here, White has just played **1. Rf2**, attacking the Black Bishop. Black cannot defend the Bishop and if it moves, the f5 Pawn will be lost. So Black plays **1...g3**, offering the Bishop as a sacrifice in order to promote a Pawn.

If White takes the Bishop with **2. Rxf4**, Black will play **2...g2**. The g-Pawn will be able to promote even though White is a Rook up because it guards f1 and the f5 Pawn controls square g4, as shown bottom right.

If White played **2. Rg2**, ignoring the Bishop, Black could play **2...Bd6+**. Black's Pawns are well advanced and supported by a Bishop so White cannot prevent promotion.

Test yourself

1. White to move. What tactic should White employ to achieve a winning position in two moves?*

2. White's move. White is seriously behind on material but can force checkmate in three moves. How?*

Sacrifices

There are two types of sacrifice: the *calculative* and the *intuitive* sacrifice. In a calculative sacrifice a piece is given up for immediate benefit — to win a piece of greater value, perhaps, or to give checkmate. There are several examples of this type of sacrifice in the previous chapter, on tactical combinations.

Intuitive sacrifice is much more complex as the gain is not immediately apparent. The benefit of an intuitive sacrifice may be, for instance, a long term attack opportunity or an improvement in the position and mobility of your pieces.

Below is a simple calculative sacrifice and the next few pages analyse a game which features an intuitive sacrifice.

Calculative sacrifice

It is White's turn to move. Black is threatening checkmate on b2 but White can take the *initiative* by sacrificing the Rook, as shown below. This sacrifice is simple and effective, and it involves no risk. Black's moves are forced, so White is sure of immediate compensation for the Rook. Remember though, even a simple sacrifice needs careful planning.

White plays **1. Rh8+!** This forces Black to take the Rook with **1...Kxh8** and diverts the action away from the vulnerable White King.

The White Queen then puts the Black King in check (**2. Qh5+**), and Black is forced to play **2...Kg8**. White now traps the King with **3. Qh7++**.

DID YOU KNOW?

• The word 'checkmate' derives from the Persian 'shah mat', meaning 'the King is dead'.

• In 1985, the Soviet player Gary Kasparov became the youngest World Champion ever at the age of 22 years, 210 days.

Intuitive sacrifice

The next few pages show a game played in 1984 by David Norwood, the author of this book and Saeed Saeed, an *International Grandmaster*. The game features an intuitive sacrifice which, together with a subsequent calculative sacrifice, wins the game for David Norwood. Norwood is playing Black and Saeed is playing White.

The game opens with a version of the Modern Benoni opening.* Both sides lose a Pawn in the struggle for central control and they both castle and *fianchetto*.

Black's plan is to exploit his Queenside strength and White wants to control the centre by bringing a Knight to c4. White's tenth move prepares for this by preventing Black from moving a Pawn to b5.

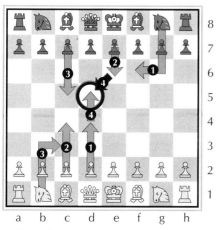

1. d4, Nf6; 2. c4, e6; 3. Nc3, c5;
4. d5, exd5.

5. cxd5, d6; 6. Nf3, g6.

7. g3, Bg7; 8. Bg2, 0-0.

9. 0-0, a6; 10. a4, Re8.

*A slightly different version of this opening appears on page 36.

The game continues

**11. Nd2, Nbd7; 12. h3, Rb8;
13. Nc4, Ne5; 14. Na3...**

In moves 11 and 13, White manoeuvres his Knight to square c4. From here it puts pressure on square d6, covers square e5 in readiness for a central Pawn advance and keeps guard on the Queenside.

By playing **13. Ne5**, Black forces White's Knight to leave its good position on c4. If White replied to this by moving **14. Nxe5**, Black would recapture with the Rook.

The White Knight has little function on the a3 square, other than to discourage Black from moving a Pawn to b5. However, White is planning to put Pawns on f4 and then e4, so that

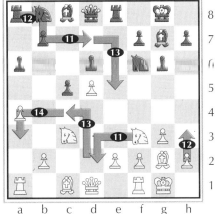

the Black Knight will retreat. After this, the White Knight will be able to resume its powerful position on c4.

Black's intuitive sacrifice

14...Bd7; 15. f4, Nh5.

Black cannot prevent White's planned Pawn advance to f4, so he reacts tactically with an intuitive sacrifice. By playing **14...Bd7**, Black removes the one retreat square available to the e5 Knight so that, after White plays **15. f4**,

16. fxe5.

16...Bxe5.

the Knight will be lost. Next, Black moves the f6 Knight to h5 so that White can capture it with **16. fxe5**. Now, the Black Bishop can take the Pawn on e5. This leaves Black a Knight for a Pawn down.

Why Black sacrificed the Knight

Black's Knight sacrifice yields no immediate benefit. However, it has left Black in a very strong position, as can be seen by studying the state of play on the board below.

Analysing the position of each side regarding piece mobility, Pawn structure, King position and possible future plans will help to clarify Black's motives for sacrificing the Knight.

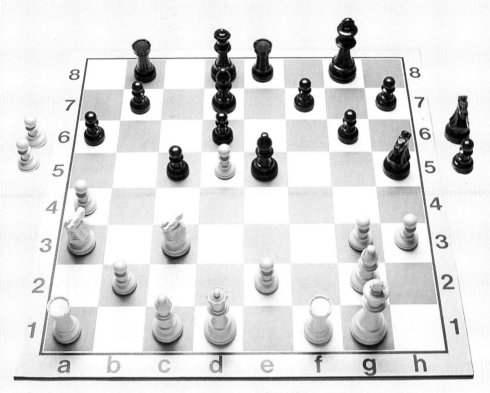

Black has:

• Captured two Pawns.
• Very good mobile pieces which control *open files* and diagonals.
• Several good plans – he can advance on the Queenside by putting a Pawn on b5, or he can play for a Kingside attack.
• Pressure on the important g3 Pawn. This Pawn covers the King and cannot be defended. If it moves to g4, the Black Knight can move to g3 and attack the White Rook.

White has:

• Captured a Pawn and a Knight.
• Weak pieces on the board, none of which are placed in useful attacking positions.
• No real plan. White's main plan to move the Pawn back to e5 is no longer feasible since it relied on the support of the f-Pawn, which is now lost.
• Bad Pawn structure with three *Pawn islands*.
• A semi-vulnerable King.

The game concludes

17. g4, Ng3.

White moves the g-Pawn to prevent Black from playing **17...Nxg3**, as this would leave Black only a point down on *material* and expose the White King. Such gains would be good compensation for the Knight sacrifice.

White's Rook on f1 is open to attack. However, if White moved it with **18. Rf2**, for example, then after **18...b5**, Black would have a good return for his sacrifice, threatening to move a Pawn to b4 to fork the Knights and advance the f-Pawn to open up the Kingside. The Black Queen could also join the attack by moving to h4.

18. Nc4, Bxc3.

Instead of moving the f1 Rook, White moves the a3 Knight to guard against Black's Queenside threats. This forces Black to change plans and capture the Knight rather than the Rook. If Black had taken the Rook, **18...Nxf1** would have led to **19. Nxe5, Rxe5; 20.Qxf1**. Material would then be equal but Black would have lost his two best attacking pieces – the Knight and the black-squared Bishop.

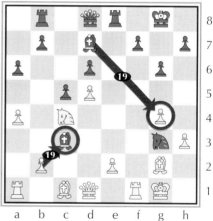

19. bxc3, Bxg4.

White recaptures with the Pawn. Black then takes the g4 Pawn and, in doing so, offers his Bishop as another powerful sacrifice. This is not an intuitive, but a calculative sacrifice as it is intended to yield immediate benefit.

Can you see what the consequences will be if White accepts the sacrifice of the Black Bishop? The answer is on the opposite page.

White takes the Bishop

20. hxg4, Nxe2+.

If White takes the Bishop, Black takes the Pawn and puts the King in check. Now, wherever the King moves it cannot escape ultimate checkmate as the Black Queen and Knight can work together to form a *mating net*. For example:

• If White plays **21. Kf2**, as below, then Black will achieve checkmate with **21…Qh4+; 22. Kf3, Qg3++**.

• If White plays **21. Kh2**, as below centre, this will lead to **21…Qh4+; 22. Bh3, Qg3+;** and **23. Kh1, Qxh3++**, as shown bottom right.

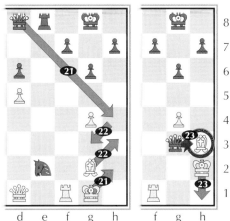

White leaves the Bishop

In fact Saeed did not accept the sacrifice of the Bishop. Even so, he could not save himself. The game continued with: **20. Qd3, Nxe2+; 21. Kh2, Nxc1; 22. Rfxc1, Be2!** White then resigned because, as soon as the Queen moved, Black could take the Knight. This would leave Black three Pawns up. In a Master-level game, this is usually enough to win.

DID YOU KNOW?

• In the Middle Ages, chess was considered too easy, so more complex versions were invented. One, Tamarlane's Chess, used a board with 110 squares. The pieces included camels and giraffes.

• The longest recorded chess match, between Yedael Stepak and Yaacov Mashian in 1981, lasted 193 moves.

Where to go from here

The most effective way to improve your game is to practise. Family and friends may be good opponents to begin with but as your standard improves it is advisable to stretch yourself by playing a wider range of players. These two pages suggest ways to find challenging opponents and learn from your experience.

Chess clubs

The best place to find other chess players is a local chess club. Chess is popular worldwide, so there should be a club near where you live. Libraries can usually provide contact addresses, or you could write to your national chess federation, listed on the right.

Correspondence chess

Another way to increase the variety of your opponents is by playing correspondence chess. This involves writing down your move and posting it to your opponent, who posts back their reply. Again, contact your chess federation for details of other players.

Chess computers

There is a huge range of chess computers on the market, for players of all levels. Many have different settings so you can increase the degree of difficulty as your standard improves. Most computers are in the form of mini-boards with magnetic sensors to register the moves. Chess programs are also available for personal computers.

Chess computers are becoming ever more sophisticated. Each year the World Microcomputer Championship is held as a challenge between the top programs. The most powerful to date is called Deep Thought. It has defeated several Grandmasters but has so far been unable to beat the current World Champion, Gary Kasparov.

Contact addresses

British Chess Federation
9a Grand Parade
St Leonards-on-Sea
East Sussex
TN38 ODD
Great Britain

English Chess Association
London Chess Centre
58 St John's Hill
London
SW11 1SF
Great Britain

The Chess Federation of Canada
2212 Gladwin Crescent E-1
Ottawa
Ontario
K1B SN1
Canada

Australian Chess Federation
c/o Larry Ermacora
GPO Box 148
Sydney
NSW 2001
Australia

New Zealand Chess Association
PO Box 40-484
Upper Hutt
Wellington
New Zealand

United States Chess Federation
Attn. Al Lawrence
186 Route 9 West
New Windsor
NY 12550
USA

Books, magazines and videos

Reading chess literature is a very effective way of increasing your knowledge of theory. There are thousands of books available, covering every aspect of chess, so the choice can be confusing. Avoid anything too specialized to begin with but look instead for general books; one on the openings and one on endgames would be a suitable start. It is also a good idea to have an up-to-date book of chess rules, as there are more than you think and they do change from time to time.

National newspaper columns are a good source of information if you want to keep abreast of international chess events. Some publish regular chess puzzles.

Specialist chess magazines are another excellent source of information. They usually list the addresses of useful contacts and suppliers.

Chess videos are available too, for those who want to see the experts in action.

Chess publishers

These publishers distribute chess literature worldwide. You can write to them for catalogues and details of your nearest stockist.

▶

Pergamon Chess
Railway Road
Sutton Coldfield
B73 6AZ
England

B T Batsford Ltd
4 Fitzhardinge Street
London
W1H 0AH
England

Learning from mistakes

As you increase your range of opponents, it is important to keep a record of the games you have played. The best way to do this is to write down all your moves, and those of your opponent, as they are made, using *algebraic notation* (see page 5). It is possible to buy score sheets like those shown here, but any piece of paper will do. Recording your games in this way will help you to identify recurring themes and recognize repeated mistakes.

It is also a good idea, as soon as you have finished a game, to analyse it with your opponent. Discuss one another's opening strategies and plans. A post-mortem is especially useful if you have lost. Ask your opponent where you went wrong – you may learn how to win next time.

* This score sheet shows part of the longest recorded game (see page 51).

	WHITE	BLACK
53	Be8	Rg2+
54	Kc1	Rg1
55	Kd2	Rg2+
56	Re2	

EVENT **Israeli Championship 1981** *
ROUND ___ DATE **Mashian**
BOARD ___
WHITE **Stepak** BLACK
GRADE ___ GRADE ___

	WHITE	BLACK		WHITE
1	d4	Nf6	27	Bg5
2	c4	e6	28	Bd2
3	Nf3	b6	29	Nh4
4	g3	Bb7	30	h3
5	Bg2	Be7	31	a4
6	Nc3	Ne4	32	Kh2
7	Qc2	Nxc3	33	Rf1
8	Qxc3	0-0	34	Qd3
9	0-0	c5	35	Nf5
10	Rd1	d6	36	Kf1
11	Qc2	Nd7	37	Rg4
12	e4	Qc7	38	Qe4
13	b3	Rfe8	39	Ke2
14	Bb2	Rad8	40	Rh2
15	Rd2	e5	41	Kd3
16	d5	Bf8	42	Kc2
17	Re2	g6	43	Kb2
				Kxg

Competitive chess

Once you have joined a chess club you will find out about the chess events and competitions in which you can take part. These two pages explain some of the procedures involved in chess tournaments. Opposite is a brief guide to gradings, and international chess.

How a tournament is run

Chess tournaments usually take place at weekends in chess clubs or town halls. Entrants are graded according to ability and play against a range of maybe five or six opponents. One point is awarded for a win and half for a draw. Winners play winners with similar scores and losers play losers. The entrant who gains the most points is the overall winner.

Time controls and chess clocks

In most competitions you will be required to play to a time limit. Each player has a specific amount of time in which to play a certain number of moves. To keep accurate track of your time you will need to use a chess clock, like the one shown here. This is a stop-clock with two faces, one to record the time you spend on your moves and one for your opponent's time. Both players set their clocks to the specified time limit. If it is your move, your clock will be ticking but your opponent's will be still. As soon as you have moved, press your clock button to stop your clock and set your

Flag drops when time is up.

opponent's ticking. If you run out of time before completing the required number of moves, you automatically lose the game.

It is up to you to notice if your opponent runs out of time, so watch out for this and keep quiet if your own time is up.

Time control tips

- When you play under a time control remember that you are fighting the clock as well as your opponent.

- Don't try to be a perfectionist, but play as good a move as possible in the time available.

- Don't spend too much time thinking about simple moves.

- Play at a steady pace; do not play too quickly but avoid being left with so little time that you have to rush your later moves. This may lead to silly mistakes.

- Be confident of your opening strategy. If you play through this quickly you will save time for later in the game.

Ending the game

There are several ways to win or draw in a game of chess. Checkmate is the ideal ending but very few advanced games actually come to this. Below are some of the more common ways for a game to end.

Offering a draw

At *Master* level the most common conclusion to a game is for one of the players to offer a draw. A draw can be offered at any point during the game but should really be suggested only if the positions are equal and neither side can gain the advantage. Beware of offering a draw if you stand any chance at all of winning.

Resigning

One sure way to lose a game is to resign. Some players do this when they feel that their position is so hopeless that it is pointless to continue. A player may indicate their resignation by tipping over their own King. It is never a good idea to resign, however, as even the most experienced player can make a blunder and even if you cannot win you may be able to play for *stalemate*.

Ways to win and draw

Win	checkmate
	opponent resigns
	opponent runs out of time
Draw	stalemate
	agreed draw
	perpetual check
	both players run out of time*
	three-fold repetition of position**

National ratings

When a tournament is organized, it is usually registered with the national chess federation. Once a player begins to compete regularly in these registered tournaments, he or she is given a rating according to performance against other rated players. Each country has its own national rating system, organized by its chess federation. The systems vary a great deal – a player may begin with a rating of 60 in one country and 200 in another. Ratings lists are usually published annually or biannually so you can measure your progress by seeing how much your rating has gone up (or down).

International chess

Above the various national rating structures is a standardized international rating system, which a player enters if he or she begins to compete at international level. This rating system is organized by *FIDE* (Fédération Internationale des Echecs), the governing body for worldwide chess. FIDE also awards the titles *FIDE Master*, *International Master*, or higher than this, *International Grandmaster*, to those people who have played consistently well against other world-class players.

Professional chess

Top chess players are paid to take part in the important tournaments and substantial prize money is awarded. This means that some players can make chess their career. Most professional players write books and articles to supplement their income but a few are able to exist solely by playing the game.

---

* This can only occur if one player fails to realize that the other has run out of time.
** This is when the players reach the same position three times in a row.

Glossary

The list of words on the next few pages explains chess terms used in this book. The page numbers in brackets direct you to the place in the book where the glossary word is most clearly defined.

Algebraic notation   A method of recording chess moves using letters for the pieces and grid references for their positions. (Page 5)

Back rank mate   Checkmate by a Queen or Rook along the eighth rank, where the King is blocked in by its own Pawns or pieces. (Page 40)

Backward Pawn   A Pawn that has trailed behind and is no longer supported by other Pawns. (Page 13)

Bad-squared Bishop   A Bishop that is blocked by its own Pawns because the Pawns are positioned on squares of the same colour as the Bishop's square. (Page 6)

Calculative sacrifice   Allowing a piece to be captured in order to gain immediate benefit in terms of **material**, mobility or attacking potential. (Page 46)

Castling   A manoeuvre in which the King moves two squares towards the side of the board and the Rook jumps over the King. Neither piece must have moved from its starting position and there must be no pieces between them. Castling cannot take place if the King has to pass over a square that is under attack. (Page 5)

Closed file   A **file** blocked by both Black and White Pawns. (Page 39)

Combination   A planned series of moves which is intended to force certain responses from the opponent, and lead them into an undesirable position. (Page 42)

Connected Pawns   Pawns adjacent to one another.

Counter gambit   A strategy in which a minor piece or Pawn is offered for **sacrifice** in response to an earlier gambit (piece offered for sacrifice) by the opponent. (Page 19)

Development   Moving pieces out to advantageous positions during the opening stage of the game. (Page 14)

Discovered attack   A tactic where one piece is moved to reveal an attack by another piece.

Discovered check   A tactic where one piece moves so that a piece behind it can give check. (Page 42)

Double check	When a piece moves to put the enemy King in check, revealing a second check by a piece behind it. (Page 63)
Double Pawns	Two Pawns of the same colour positioned one in front of the other. (Page 13)
Double Rooks	Two Rooks of the same colour positioned on the same **rank** or **file**. (Page 7)
Endgame	The closing stage of a game, when few pieces are left on the board. (Page 4)
En passant	A rule which allows a Pawn to capture an enemy Pawn that has moved two squares, as though it has moved only one square.
Equalize	Make a move that balances the strengths and weaknesses of either side, so that, at that point, both sides have an equal chance of winning. (Page 21)
Exchange	Trading a piece for an enemy piece, or pieces, of equal value. (Page 9)
Exchange advantage	Trading a piece for an enemy piece, or pieces, of greater value. (Page 9)
Fair exchange	Same as **Exchange**. Trading a piece for an enemy piece, or pieces, of equal value.
Fianchetto	A manoeuvre where the Pawn in front of the Knight is moved one square and the Bishop is moved to the Pawn's position. From there, the Bishop controls the longest diagonal on the board and is protected by Pawns in front and on both sides. (Page 6)
FIDE	Fédération Internationale des Echecs. The world chess federation which organizes the international rating system, awards and titles. (Page 55)
FIDE Master	Title awarded by FIDE, ranked below **International Master**. (Page 55)
File	A column of squares running from the top of the board to the bottom. The files are lettered a–h in algebraic notation. (Page 5)
Fixed Pawn	A Pawn whose advance is blocked by an enemy piece. (Page 13)
Forced mate	A sequence of moves that will lead to checkmate, irrespective of the opponent's responses.

Fork	A simultaneous attack on two pieces by one enemy piece. (Page 43)
Gambit	An opening strategy, offering the sacrifice of a **minor piece**, or Pawn, in order to achieve good development. (Page 18)
Good-squared Bishop	A Bishop that is mobile because it is positioned on a square of the opposite colour to the squares on which most of its Pawns are stationed. (Page 6)
Hanging Pawns	Two Pawns on adjacent **files** that have no enemy Pawns ahead of them and no friendly Pawns on the files to either side. (Page 13)
Initiative, have the	To lead the game with threatening moves so that your opponent has to respond with defensive moves. (Page 15)
International Grandmaster	A title awarded by FIDE for consistent excellent play at international level. (Page 55)
International Master	A title awarded by FIDE. Not as high a title as **International Grandmaster**. (Page 55)
Intuitive sacrifice	Surrendering a piece in order to gain the advantage in the long term, but bringing no immediate benefit. (Page 47)
Isolated Pawn	A Pawn that has no neighbouring Pawns on the **files** adjacent to it. (Page 13)
Kingside	**Files** e–h on the board. (Page 5)
Lose a tempo	Neglect to make a move within an active area of the board; this may sometimes be intentional as it can strengthen your position. (Page 29)
Major piece	A Queen or Rook. (Page 13)
Material	The total value in points of a player's pieces on the board. (Page 9)
Material advantage	Greater strength in terms of the value, in points, of the pieces on the board. (Page 10)
Material disadvantage	Less strength than your opponent in terms of the total value, in points, of your pieces on the board. (Page 9)
Mating net	Pieces working together to trap and checkmate the enemy King. (Page 32)

Middlegame	The stage of the game after the opening and before the **endgame**, when most pieces are **exchanged**. (Page 4)
Minor piece	A Bishop or a Knight.
Open file	A **file** on which there are no Pawns. A file is still open even if it is occupied by pieces other than Pawns. (Page 7)
Opening	The first stage of a game, from move one until piece development is complete. (Page 4)
Opposition, have the	To move your King so that it faces the enemy King on the same **file** with only one square separating them, so the enemy King has to move back or sideways. (Page 29)
Overloaded	A piece which is defending too many pieces at once. (Page 24)
Passed Pawn	A Pawn that will not encounter enemy Pawns on its own or an adjacent **file** on its way to the other end of the board. (Page 12)
Pawn break	The possibility of opening up a blocked **Pawn structure** by advancing a Pawn.
Pawn centre	A pair or group of Pawns of the same colour that occupy the central squares of the board. (Page 23)
Pawn chain	A string of two or more Pawns of the same colour along a diagonal. (Page 12)
Pawn island	A Pawn or group of Pawns separated from other Pawns of the same colour. (Page 12)
Pawn structure	The arrangement of a player's Pawns on the board. (Page 11)
Perpetual check	When a player is put in check repeatedly but cannot be checkmated. In this event the game is agreed drawn.
Piece	Any chess piece other than the Pawn, but usually referring to a Knight or Bishop.
Piece value	The value in points of a piece according to how powerful it is. Queen = 9 points; Rook = 5 points; Bishop = 3 points; Knight = 3 points; Pawn = 1 point; King has no point value. (Page 9)
Pin	An attack on a piece that is shielding another piece of greater value. The pinned piece must remain in position or else expose the more valuable piece to attack. (Page 43)

Positional advantage	Pieces positioned so that they have more mobility and potential than those of the opponent. Key factors are good **Pawn structure**, control of **open files** and diagonals, and a mobile Bishop. (Page 17)
Promote a Pawn	Make a Pawn into a more powerful piece (usually a Queen, or sometimes a Knight) when it reaches the other end of the board. (Page 28)
Queening square	The square which a Pawn must reach in order for it to **promote**. (Page 29)
Queenside	**Files** a–d on the board. (Page 5)
Rank	A row of squares running across the board, numbered 1–8 in algebraic notation. (Page 5)
Resign	To admit defeat when you think you cannot win the game. (Page 57)
Sacrifice	To give up material in the belief that this will improve your position in the short or long term. (Page 9)
Semi-open file	A **file** in front of a Queen or Rook that is occupied by just one enemy Pawn and none of your own. A file is still semi-open even if it contains pieces other than the Pawn. (Page 37)
Skewer	An attack which forces a valuable piece to move and so reveals an attack on a piece of less value.
Smothered mate	Checkmate with a Knight when the King is blocked in by its own pieces. (Page 63)
Space advantage	Controlling a greater area of the board, allowing more space to manoeuvre.
Stalemate	A situation where the player whose turn it is next can make no legal move but is not in check. This ends the game immediately as a draw. (Page 33)
Trade	See **Exchange**.
Triple Pawns	Three Pawns of the same colour positioned along a **file**, one in front of the other. (Page 13)
Underpromote	**Promote a Pawn** to a piece other than a Queen. (Page 62)
Zugzwang	A position where every legal move a player can make leads to a substantially worse position or defeat. It is common for a player to resign when in zugzwang.

Puzzle answers

Page 10

1. White is stronger. The White Knight is mobile but the Black Bishop is blocked in by its own Pawns.

2. Black should move **1...Nxd3**. The Knight will then be taken by the White Queen but Black will have the *exchange advantage* and the stronger position. White will be left with a *bad-squared Bishop* which is unable to attack Black's strong, centrally placed Knight.

3. Black should move the Queen to a5, putting the White King in check. Black then has to move out of check and the White Queen can take the Bishop on g5.

4. White should move the Queen to d4 to put the Black King in check. Black is then forced to move the King and the White Queen can capture the b2 Rook.

5. White should move **1. Bh3** to attack the Black Knight. The Knight will be forced to remain in position to shield the Rook on c8 – this is called a *pin*. If Black tries to defend with **1...Rd8**, then **2. Nc6** will ensure that the Knight is captured.

6. Black can play **1...Rh1**, moving the Rook to put the White King in check. White is forced to move the King to the g-file. Black can then force the King back to the h-file ▼

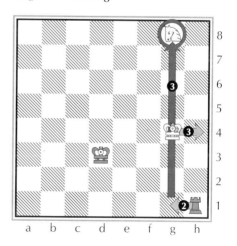

Page 27

1. Black should play **1...Rc2**. With this move the Rook attacks both the White Pawn and Queen. When the Queen moves out of danger the Rook can capture the Pawn.

2. White should capture the black-squared Bishop on g7. Most of the Black Pawns are on white squares, so this Bishop is very powerful.

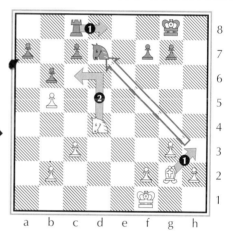

with **2...Rg1** and go on to capture the Knight with **3...Rxg8**.

Puzzle answers continued

Page 31

If White moved the Rook from the a-file, the Black Rook could leave its defending position and the a2 Pawn could *promote*.

If the White King moved **1. Kf3**, this would allow Black's Pawn to promote with **1...Rf1+; 2. Ke3, a1(Q)**.

▼

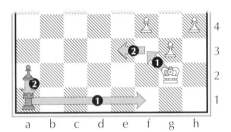

If, on the other hand, White moved **1. Kf2**, the White Rook would be lost with **1...Rh1!; 2. Rxa2, Rh2+; 3. Kg1, Rxa2.**

▼

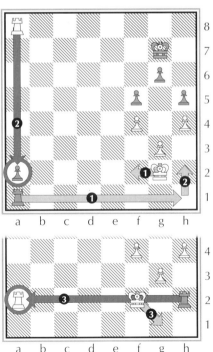

Page 34

1. White should play **1. h3** as this leads to **1...Kh8; 2. h4, Kg8; 3. h5, Kh8; 4. g6, hxg6; 5. hxg6, Kg8; 6. g7, Kf7** and the Pawn can now promote, as shown below. (Note that if White played **1. h4**, this would lead to **1...Kh8; 2. h5, Kg8; 3. g6, hxg6; 4. hxg6, Kh8=.**)

▼

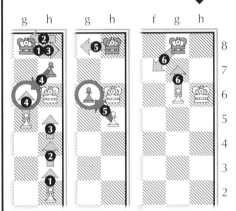

2. White should *underpromote* with **1. e8(N)+**. If White promoted to a Queen, Black would give checkmate with **1...Ra8**. By promoting to a Knight, White puts the Black King in check and forces it to move. This breaks the *mating net*, which relied on the two Kings facing each other. Now, with accurate play, White can draw.

▼

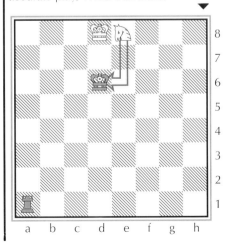

Page 37

Black can support the b-Pawn by putting a Rook on b8. White can support the Pawn advance to e5 by moving the d2 Knight to c4 or f3 and bringing the Rook to e1.

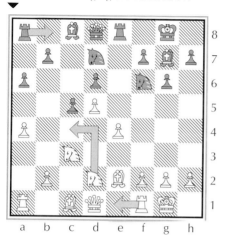

Page 39

1. White could bring both Rooks to the d-file, put a Bishop on f3 and attack the pieces which are defending Black's d5 Pawn.

2. The King is exposed along the g-file so it would be a good idea to put a Rook on this file. The best way to do this would be to play **1. Re3** followed by **2. Rg3+**.

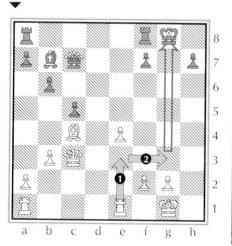

Page 45

1. White should play **1. Rxe7**. This tactic involves *overloading* the f8 Bishop – it cannot defend the Knight on e7 and guard against checkmate from g7 too. After **1...Bxe7**, White can play **2. Qg7++**.

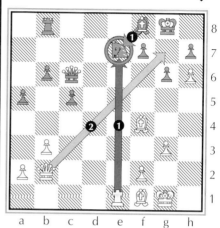

2. White should play **1. Nh6+**. This is a *double check* – the Knight has put the King in check and revealed a *discovered check* by the Queen. The King must move **1...Kh8**. Now White can play **2. Qg8+** and the Rook is forced to capture the Queen (**2...Rxg8**). Now White can move **3. Nf7++**. This is called a *smothered mate* as the checkmated King is hemmed-in by its own pieces.

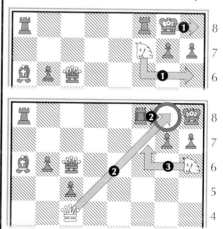

Index

Page numbers printed in italics indicate glossary references.

Part Two

CHESS PUZZLES

David Norwood

Edited by Lisa Watts and Carol Varley
Designed by Fiona Brown
Illustrated by Ian Winter

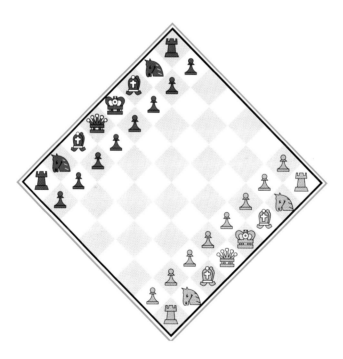

Additional illustrations by Susannah English

With thanks to Frank Van Hasselt

Contents

Thank you to Peter Wells, Talal Ja'bari, Tim Barker, Sam Pickles
and James Thacker for checking the puzzles in this book.

Susannah English is represented by the Steven Wells Illustration Agency.

Using part two

Working on the puzzles in part two will help you to improve your chess skills, giving you lots of practice in finding solutions for tricky chess positions that may occur in your games.

The puzzles at the beginning are easier than those later on, so working through the earlier puzzles will help you to build up the experience you need to tackle the more difficult ones.

Following the puzzles

Each puzzle is illustrated with a chess board using the piece symbols shown on the right. Chess moves are indicated by red or green arrows on the boards, as shown below.

The moves are written in algebraic notation, which is explained on page 128. If you come across a chess term you don't understand, turn to the glossary in part one (pages 56-60).

A move   An attack   A capture

King   Queen

Rook   Bishop

Knight   Pawn

Answers, clues and tips

Some of the puzzles have clues to help you spot key features. These puzzles are marked with the symbol shown on the right. The clues are on pages 104-107.

The puzzle answers, along with detailed explanations can be found on pages 108-125.

There are Puzzle Master tips on many pages too, giving general hints on how to improve your puzzle-solving skills.

Solving the puzzles

You may be able to solve some of the easier puzzles just by studying the diagrams in the book, but for the more difficult puzzles, you will need to set up the position on a chess board.

Some of the puzzles are real brainteasers, so it is a good idea to set up the position and keep returning to it when you have a new idea, or discuss it with friends.

Do not worry, though, if you cannot solve all the puzzles. It can be just as satisfying to study the answer and follow it on your chess board.

Pawn puzzles

The Pawn is the weakest piece, but if a Pawn reaches the other end of the board it can be promoted to a Queen or any other piece. At the beginning of the game, Pawns usually move out to open the lines and defend the centre of the board. Later on, they become more active.

1

Black has one Pawn and White has three, but Black's Pawn is more powerful. Can you see why?

2

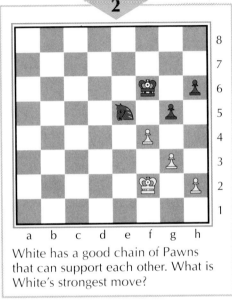

White has a good chain of Pawns that can support each other. What is White's strongest move?

3

This diagram shows all the possible moves for the White Pawn on g2. Which do you think is the best move: **1.g3**, **1.g4** or **1.gxh3**?

4

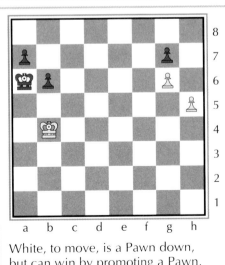

White, to move, is a Pawn down, but can win by promoting a Pawn. Which of the two Pawns can White promote in three moves?

Knight puzzles

The Knight can hop over pieces, so it is mobile early in the game. It can also stage surprise attacks from behind other pieces. The Knight is more powerful in the centre of the board, from where it can move to more squares, than when it is placed near the edge of the board.

1

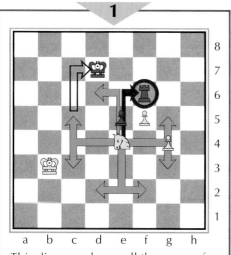

This diagram shows all the moves for the White Knight on e4. Which is the best move?

2

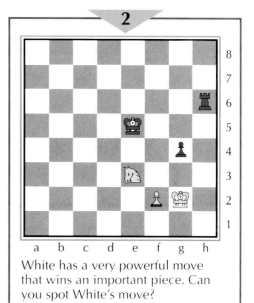

White has a very powerful move that wins an important piece. Can you spot White's move?

3

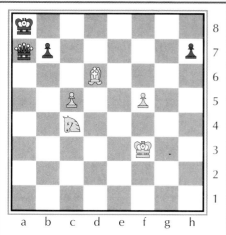

Can you spot a move for the White Knight that will allow White to win an important piece next turn?

4

Black has no Queen but the Black Knight can give mate in two different ways. Can you find both ways?

Bishop puzzles

In general, the Bishop is as valuable as the Knight, but it cannot hop over other pieces so it can be clumsy in closed positions. On open lines, though, the Bishop can dominate the game for, unlike the Knight, it can sweep from one side of the board to the other.

1

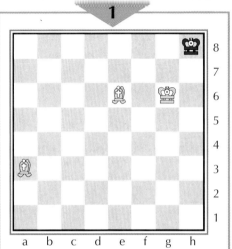

Two Bishops can be a devastating force. Here, they have driven the King into a corner and are ready for mate. Can you see how?

2

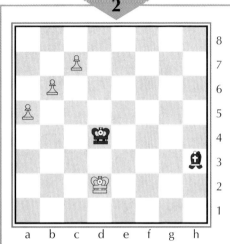

Black is in trouble. White's Pawns are very close to promoting. Can you find a way for Black to save the game and force a draw?

3

Black is a Pawn down but can come back with a vengeance. Can you spot Black's best move?

4

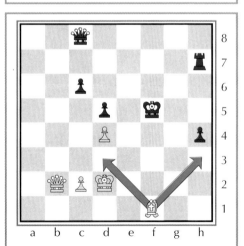

The White Bishop can make two good moves: **1.Bh3+** or **1.Bd3+**. Which would you choose?

Rook puzzles

A Rook is more powerful than either a Knight or a Bishop. In an endgame when there are no other pieces on the board, a King and a Rook can mate an enemy King, whereas a King and Knight, or King and Bishop, cannot. Rooks are most powerful on open lines.

1

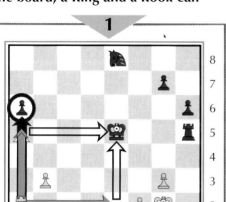

White is a Knight down, but has a strong Rook that can move along open lines. Which is the best Rook move: **1.Re2+**, **1.Ra5+** or **1.Rxa6**?

2

The Black King has a Knight to defend it, but White can win the Knight in three moves. Can you see how? White to move.

3

On this board, the Black King and Rook are about to mate the enemy King. Can you see how?

4

Here, White is confronted by two enemy Rooks and Black has a very strong move. Can you spot it?

Queen puzzles

The Queen is the most mobile piece on the board, and a powerful attacking piece. Like the Bishop, it can sweep along diagonals and, like the Rook, it can move horizontally and vertically. This is why players choose to promote a Pawn to a Queen in most cases.

1

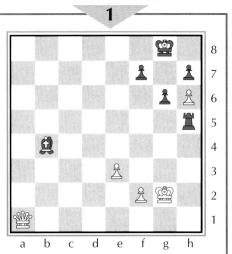

The Queen is a good piece with which to play for mate. Here, White can finish off Black with one move. Make sure you choose the right one.

2

The White Queen can check the Black King in many ways – and take a piece each time. How many ways can you see?

3

White can check the King and then win the Knight or Rook – but only one can be taken safely. Which one?

4

Black's next move checkmates the White King. What is Black's mating move?

King puzzles

Usually, you should guard your King, but sometimes, especially in the endgame, you can use the King more actively to help give checkmate and win material.

1

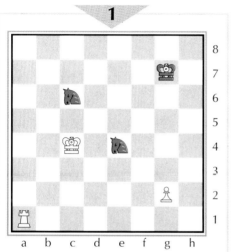

How can White win material in this position?

2

Black has a brilliant King move. Can you spot it?

3

Here, White can give checkmate in one move – you need to think carefully about this one.

4

This is a tricky one. Can you find a two-move mating sequence for White? White to move.

Checkmate in one

In the puzzles on these two pages you have to find a way to deliver mate in one move. There are some general tips to help you on the opposite page and there are clues to specific puzzles on page 104.

1

Just in case you think mate in one is too easy, the position above is from a game in which a Grandmaster missed White's winning move. Can you find it?

2

In this game played by our author, David Norwood, and a Russian Grandmaster, Norwood (Black) played **1...Kd5**, and was shocked by White's reply. What was it?

3

On this board, whoever moves, wins. Can you spot a mate for Black and one for White?

4

The Black King looks vulnerable, but there is only one way to finish Black off. What is it?

5

On this board, White can use the pin attack to great advantage. Can you spot White's mate?

6

Black has some good moves on this board. Can you spot the tactic that finishes the game immediately?

Puzzle Master tips

• Consider all possible moves – the most brilliant solutions are often the least obvious ones.

• When planning mate, try to cut off all the enemy King's escape squares.

• Look out for skewers, forks and pins to use to your advantage.

7

There is no doubt about the outcome of this game, as White has a much stonger army than Black. But finding mate in one move is not easy for White. Can you spot it?

8

In this game, White, a young chess star, was mated in the opening. White greedily captured the Black Bishop on b4. How did Black teach White a lesson?

Two-move mates

In each of these puzzles you need to think a little further and find a sequence of two moves that leads to mate. After the first move and your opponent's reply, your second move should give checkmate.

1

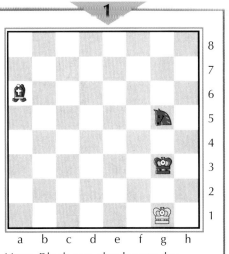

Here, Black can checkmate the White King in the corner in just two moves. Black to move.

2

Black is in trouble. How can the White Knights be used to deliver checkmate? White to move.

3

Both sides have the same pieces and the Pawn structure is symmetrical, but White's Rooks are better placed on open lines. How can White deliver mate in two?

4

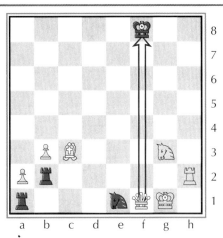

Here, Black is in check – but remember, moving the King is not always the best escape from check. How can Black go on the attack and give mate in two?

5

This tricky puzzle is taken from a real game situation. Can you spot White's brilliant two-move mate?

6

Here, White has an extra Bishop, but there is only one way for White to mate in two. What is it?

On this board, White has *fianchettoed* in front of the King and then lost the *fianchetto* Bishop. How can Black use this situation to deliver mate in two?

7

Combinations which require simple moves are often the hardest to spot. Here, White's position looks desperate, but with a sharp eye you could save it. White to move.

8

More two-movers

The puzzles on these two pages are a little more difficult. In the four below, you do not know whose move it is. On each board, either

Black or White is about to mate the enemy King in two moves. If you get stuck, turn to the clues on page 104 to find out whose move it is.

On this board, White still has a Queen, while Black has a powerful pair of Bishops. Which of the two can bring about a two-move mate?

White certainly has more pieces – an extra Rook and three Pawns – but are you sure it is White and not Black who has the mate?

Black is a Rook down but has a strong Queen. Who do you think can win on this board?

This puzzle may look confusing – but remember, it is often the most innocent-looking move that is best.

Two moves – two solutions

This time you are told which side can give mate in two, but each puzzle has two solutions, that is, the winning side can mate in two different ways.

5

White has more pieces and seems to be doing well, but Black has two different ways to deliver mate in two. Can you find them?

Puzzle Master tips

● When trying to find mate, look at the enemy King's escape squares and decide which of your pieces are attacking, or can attack, those squares.

● If your opponent's pieces are blocking their own King's escape squares, see if you can use this to your advantage.

● Try to ensnare the enemy King in a position where the King is trapped by pieces of either colour. You can then move in to attack the King and deliver mate.

DID YOU KNOW? The Queen and Bishop were not introduced into the game of chess until 1475. For some time, the new game was sneeringly called the "mad Queen" version, until people realized how much more exciting it was.

White has two strong mating combinations – one of which involves a sacrifice. Can you spot the two different ways in which White can give mate in two moves?

6

Tactics and combinations

Before you can deliver mate, you usually need to weaken your opponent's army by winning pieces. In these puzzles, see if you can win material with a two- or three-move combination. Look out for pins, skewers, sacrifices and other tactics to use to your advantage.

1

How does the awkward placing of Black's King and Rooks allow White to win an important piece in three moves? White to move.

2

White has played **1.Bb4**, pinning Black's Queen. Can you spot a three-move combination for Black that leaves Black a Pawn and Bishop up?

3

Can you find a clever combination which will win a Pawn for Black? Black to move.

4

Black's Knight is attacked, but Black is only too willing to move it. What is Black's winning combination?

White is behind on material (White has 8 points, Black has 11), but White can gain the material advantage by sacrificing a piece. Can you spot White's tactical two-move ploy? (For more about point values, see page 9.)

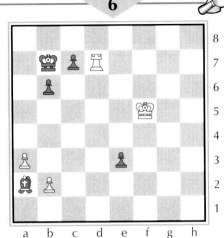

6

Black's Pawn on e3 is close to promoting, but if Black plays **1...e2**, White can stop the Pawn with **2.Re7**. Can you spot a different combination for Black that leaves White helpless to stop the Pawn promoting?

In this Rook and Pawn endgame, the Black Rook has lined up behind the White a-Pawn in an attempt to stop it from promoting. Can you find a tactical three-move combination for White that leaves White a Rook up?

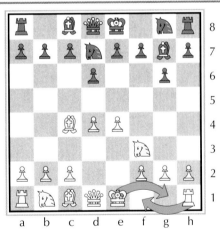

On this board, David Norwood, our author, had Black and was happy to see his opponent castle. He realized that White had missed an excellent chance to win material and open up the defences around the Black King. What was it?

Sacrifice to win

No one likes to lose a piece, but sometimes it can be well worth your while. In the puzzles on these two pages, you again have to work out how to mate the enemy King in two moves. This time, though, it is not possible to achieve mate without making a sacrifice.

1

White is two pieces down, having lost both Bishops. Can you see how White can sacrifice a piece to deliver mate on the second move?

2

The White King is defended by only a thin line of Pawns. Can you spot a sacrifice for Black that leads to mate on the second move?

3

In this puzzle, White can sacrifice a piece to free another piece to deal the final blow. Can you see how?

4

Our author, playing White, was three Pawns down but he had a winning sacrifice. Can you spot it?

White's King is in a tight spot, but there is only one way for Black to mate in two and it involves a sacrifice. Black to move.

Even though White has a Knight and Black has a Queen, White has a forceful solution. Can you see how White can mate in two moves?

DID YOU KNOW? The game of chess has a ruling goddess called Caissa. She was first introduced in a poem by Sir William Jones in 1763, where she is described as a beautiful nymph, admired and pursued by the great god Mars. In the poem, Mars invents the game of chess in an attempt to win Caissa's heart.

White can trap Black in a smothered mate. Which piece should White sacrifice, and what are the two moves to mate?

White's pieces are bearing down on Black's King and, by sacrificing a piece, White can deliver mate in two moves. Can you see how?

Study puzzles

In chess terminology, a study is a chess position that has been set up to create a challenging puzzle. Studies are quite difficult and require all your chess skills. There are some tips to help you below.

Puzzle Master tips

Because a study has been specially designed as a puzzle, the pieces are often in an unusual arrangement that is unlikely to occur in an actual game. Studies also tend to have unusual or even bizarre solutions – for example, it is often a humble Pawn or an oddly positioned piece that actually delivers mate. Studies are therefore a good way to practise lateral thinking when approaching chess problems. Here are some tips for solving studies.

● First, from the arrangement of the pieces, identify that the problem is probably a study and be prepared to look for an unusual solution.

● Study the position of each piece – it has been placed there for a particular reason. Look carefully at any piece whose role is not so obvious, as it may be the key to the answer.

● Try to work out the mating net, or the square on which the King could be mated, then work backwards to see how the mate could be brought about. (For more practice in solving puzzles by working backwards, see Retro-puzzles, pages 92–93.)

● Be cunning. Studies require skilful manoeuvres rather than obvious attacking or checking moves. For example, a placid waiting move may cause the enemy King to become trapped among its own pieces.

Here, White can capture the Queen or promote a Pawn, but for White to mate in two, a more unusual solution is required.

White is winning and the logical move is to save the Rook on a2. Instead, White can attack and reach mate in two. Can you see how?

3

White has to play a peculiar move to force mate in two – moving a piece away from an attacking position and leaving another piece unprotected. How can White complete the mating net around the King and force mate in two?

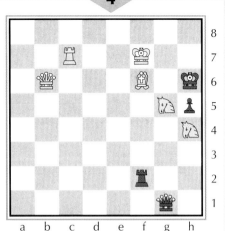

White's most obvious moves are with the major pieces but, in fact, a quiet move by the White King is the key to the solution. Again, try to deliver mate in two by completing the mating net around the Black King and cutting off its escape squares.

This is a difficult study. For White to mate in two, you need to find a quiet move that will put Black in *zugzwang*, so that whatever Black does, mate is inevitable. As in Puzzle 3, you need to move a piece away from an attacking position so that White can deliver mate on move two.

Although the position on this board looks as though it could have been designed as a study, it occurred in one of the author's games. David Norwood, playing White, was unable to find a mate in two. Can you spot the move that leads to mate the following move?

Save yourself puzzles

Sometimes your position is so bad that the best you can aim for is a draw – a way to avoid losing the game. There are two obvious ways of doing this – with perpetual check or stalemate. Can you save yourself in the puzzles on these two pages?

Ways to draw

● Perpetual check is a position where a King cannot escape constant checks.

● In stalemate, the player whose turn it is to move next can make no legal move, but is not in check. You can force stalemate by positioning your pieces so that your opponent's moves leave *you* with no legal reply, or you can try to create a position where *your opponent* has no legal move.

1

On this board, Black has just moved the Rook to f8 and expects White to resign. It is possible, however, for White to force a draw. Can you see how?

This puzzle has two parts:
a) White is a Queen, a Bishop and two Pawns down, yet can salvage a draw. Can you see how?
b) Now imagine the position without the Pawn on e5. Can White still force a draw?

2

Black is in trouble. The White a-Pawn is advancing up the board and the Black King cannot catch it before it promotes. Can you see how Black, in four moves, manages to create a position which is a draw? Black to move.

3

The position shown on the board below is from a game played in 1958 by Khalomoyez and Gurin, two Soviet Masters, in Simferopol, in the Soviet Union. Gurin, playing Black, saw that his Pawn was attacked and decided to push it to g1 and promote it.

The Pawn can be promoted to a Knight, Bishop, Rook or Queen. You might think that Black could not help but win with so many options. White, however, has a good defence whichever piece Black chooses – and, in some cases, can even win.

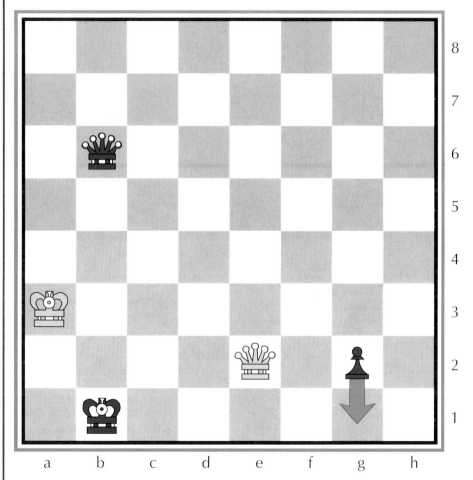

For each piece to which the Pawn can be promoted (the options are shown below), what is White's defence, and in each case, how will the game end?

a) Pawn to Knight

b) Pawn to Bishop

c) Pawn to Rook

d) Pawn to Queen

Advanced winning techniques

So far, most of the puzzles have involved combinations of one or two moves. But to become a Puzzle Master you must be able to think a little deeper. In the following problems you need to find mating combinations of three or four moves.

With longer combinations it is impossible to analyse every possible move – there are too many. Instead, look for a winning strategy, such as those listed in the tips below.

Puzzle Master tips

● Look at your own position before you go on the attack. Are you in danger yourself? If your opponent has a mating move, your first priority is to prevent this.

● Examine the position of the enemy King. Does it look exposed or trapped, perhaps on the back rank? Can you lure, rather than force, the enemy King into a mating net?

● Look for pieces to sacrifice to improve your position or trap the enemy King.

● Can you win material with a tactical trick such as a check, pin, skewer or fork?

● Look for forcing moves, such as checks, that leave your opponent with only a limited number of replies. It is easier to plan long combinations if you can predict your opponent's responses.

This position is from a game played in 1852 between two German world class players: A. Anderssen and J. Dufresne. Anderssen, playing White, spotted a brilliant mating combination. Can you find a mate for White in three or four moves? White to move.

It is White's move and many a strong player would play **1.gxf3**. A Puzzle Master, though, would realize that the White Bishop and Knight are ready to attack the King and that a mate may be in sight. Can you find the devastating move for White that leads to mate in up to four moves?

1

2

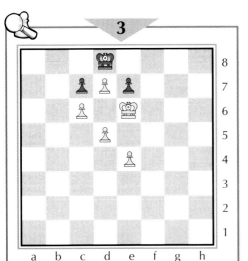

3

This is a tricky puzzle. White, with two extra Pawns, is winning, and your task is to mate Black in four moves. It is White's move and the main problem is to avoid putting Black in stalemate. If you can keep Black on the move, you should be able to deliver mate in four. Be careful not to give Black too much freedom, though.

4

Black's King is exposed and the Black Queen and the Rook on a7 are blocked and out of play. White can deliver mate in four moves, but to find the mating combination you need to spot clever Queen moves for White on moves two and three. Move two is an ordinary check and move three threatens mate in two different ways. White moves first.

5

This position is taken from the chess notebook of an Italian Master, Damiano, and dates from 1512. Can you find White's three-move mating combination? White to move.

6

Black has a winning move, to which White can reply in various ways. Analyse White's defences carefully to find a mate for Black in up to four moves. Black to move.

Help-mate puzzles

In the puzzles on these two pages, the aim is not to defeat your opponent but to defeat yourself! You have to find a sequence of moves that will enable your opponent to mate you. Many of the world's leading Grandmasters claim that composing and solving help-mate puzzles helps them to play better chess.

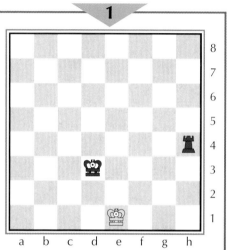

1

Here is an easy example to start with. White, to move, has a help-mate in one. That is, in one move, White moves to a position where Black can give checkmate. Can you spot White's move?

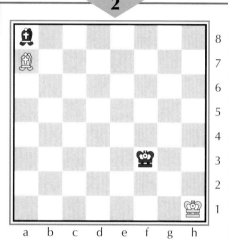

2

This puzzle is a little harder but you still only need to think one move ahead. White, to move, has a help-mate in one. Can you see a move for White that allows Black to achieve checkmate next move?

In this puzzle, White has a help-mate in two: White plays a move, Black replies, White plays another move and Black delivers checkmate. Black has only a King and a Knight, and an endgame with a King and a Knight against a lone King is always a draw. On this board, though, White also has a Rook – and that makes all the difference. Can you see how Black, with White's help, is able to deliver mate on the second move? White to move.

3

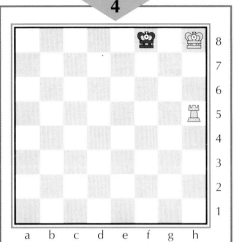

4

In this position, Black has a help-mate in three. To deliver checkmate, White has to make active use of both the King and the Rook. The trick is to try to move the White King on to a useful square while manoeuvring the Black King on to a vulnerable one. Black to move.

5

On this board, White has a help-mate in five. But do not worry – long puzzles are not always the most difficult. In this puzzle, once you have worked out how to drive the White King to a vulnerable square, delivering mate is quite easy. White to move.

Puzzle Master tips

- Decide which squares are attacked by the mating side's pieces and try to organize the pieces to form a mating net.

- Look for a vulnerable square for your King – a corner for example, or near the edge of the board.

- Remember, one of the most common mates is a back rank mate, where the King is trapped on the first rank by its own pieces. Can you manoeuvre the pieces to trap your King?

This puzzle is quite difficult. White has a help-mate in three. The trick is to imagine a position in which White can be mated, and the first thing to notice is that the Black King is too far away to help. Can you find a way for the Black Rook, on its own, to mate the White King? White to play.

6

Retro-puzzles

Retro means backwards, and in these puzzles you have to be a detective and work out what has happened in the game so far. By observing which pieces have moved and which have been captured, you can deduce which moves might have taken place. But be careful, in retro-puzzles, things are not always as simple as they seem...

1

On the board below, your task is to work out which piece, or pieces, could have captured the Black Knight. To find this out, you need to decide what has happened on the board up until now.

In fact, very little appears to have happened. All you can say with certainty is that the White Bishop and Black Knight have been captured, and that the Bishop must have been taken on a6 by the b7 Pawn. You can be sure of this because Pawns do not lie. A Pawn cannot move backwards and if a Pawn has moved diagonally, it must have made a capture. Black's doubled Pawns on a6 and a7 show that a capture must have taken place, and the Bishop is the only White piece that is missing.

But what about the Black Knight? You may be tempted to think that the Black Knight was captured on a6 by the Bishop, and the Bishop was then taken by the Pawn – but you have no proof. The Knight could, for example, have been taken by the White Queen, which then returned to its own square, while the Bishop voluntarily moved to a6 and was captured by the Pawn.

Now, remembering that Pawns do not lie, can you deduce which pieces might, according to the rules of chess, have captured the Black Knight?

Puzzle Master tip

In retro-puzzles, forget about the probable and think about the possible.

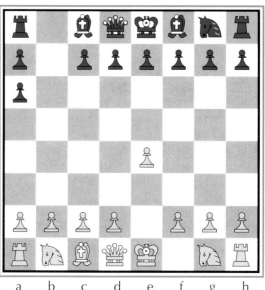

Who took the Black Knight?

Did the White Queen capture the Knight?

Could the King have captured the Knight?

Are the Bishops guilty?

Could the Rooks have moved?

One day, Mr White and Mrs Black visited their local chess club and sat at a table in the corner. On this table there was a chess board, on which the position shown on the board below had been reached by two young players. The players had abandoned their game so Mr White and Mrs Black decided to take up where they had left off.

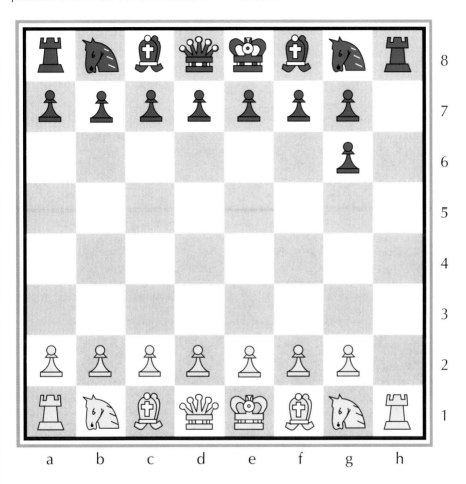

Mr White chose White and Mrs Black chose Black and the game continued until Mr White decided to castle. At this point, Mrs Black protested that White could not castle.

"Can't castle?" grumbled Mr White.

"It's not allowed," said Mrs Black. "You've already moved your Rook, the one on h1."

"I have?" said Mr White. "How do you know?"

"Look at the position with which we started," replied Mrs Black. "It couldn't have been reached without any Rook moves."

Was Mrs Black right? Has the Rook on h1 already moved or not? And if it has, how did you work it out?

Brainteasers

Here are some slightly unusual puzzles to test your chess skills. Working on unorthodox studies like these helps to improve your problem-solving skills by encouraging you to think of unusual solutions.

1

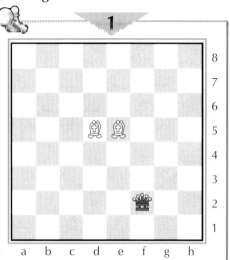

Of course, this board position could not be from a real game – there are no Kings. Your task is to place the Kings so that White, to move, puts Black in checkmate. Try to find the most vulnerable square for the Black King and position the White King so it can deliver mate with the help of the two Bishops.

2

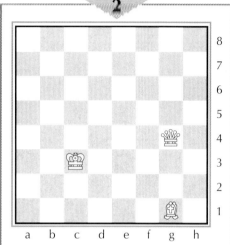

Here is a another classic study. On this board, your task is to find three different positions for the Black King. See if you can place the King so that it is:

a) in checkmate.
b) in stalemate.
c) about to be mated by White's next move.

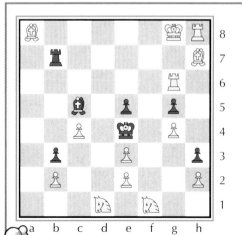

In this puzzle, you have to find a way for White *not* to deliver mate. It seems that every move White can make puts Black in checkmate. Can you find the one White move that keeps Black in the game?

3

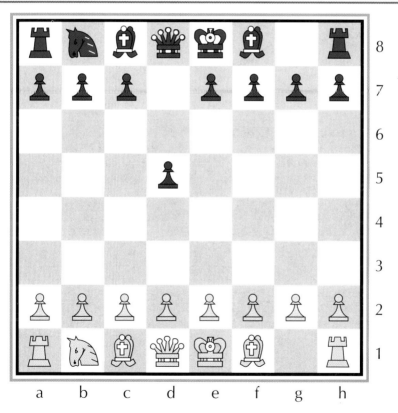

● William the Conqueror once broke a chess board over his opponent's head. This weapon was used by a French knight, Renaud de Montauban, with even more dramatic effect – he killed his opponent.

● In 1914, a German chess magazine reported a particularly tricky retro-puzzle. The solver was given a board position and had to work out whose move it was next. The only way to find the answer was to work backwards 53 moves to the beginning of the game.

CHESS QUOTES

"Chess is a fine entertainment."
Leo Tolstoy

"Chess is too difficult to be a game, and not serious enough to be a science or an art."   Napoleon Bonaparte

"Chess is life."   Bobby Fischer

"Chess is vanity."
Alexander Alekhine

"Chess is a sad waste of brains."
Sir Walter Scott

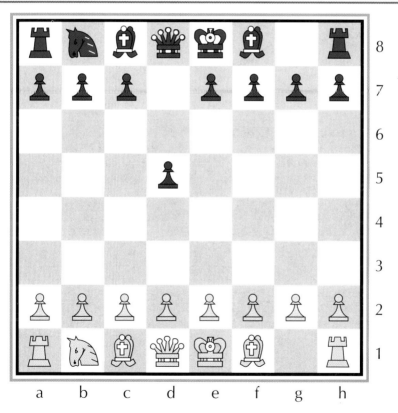

This puzzle requires some of the retro-analytical skills that you used in the puzzles on the previous two pages. Each side has played just four moves. Can you work out what they were? In fact, there are several possibilities, all leading to the position shown above, with Black and White both losing a Knight. White moves first.

4

Mate the Grandmaster

All these positions are from real game situations in which a Grandmaster was, or could have been, checkmated. Imagine you are a world class Master and see if you can checkmate the Grandmaster.

1

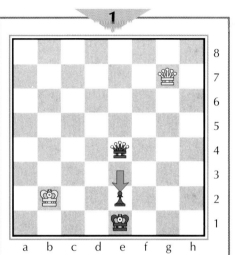

This board is from a game between two Soviet Masters, Babuyev and Smagin, played in Riga, in 1954. Smagin, playing Black, has just advanced his Pawn to e2 and is expecting victory. If you were playing White, how would you checkmate him?

2

This position is from a game between Frazekas and Speelman in 1938. White's position looks hopeless: his Queen is threatened and Black is also threatening to capture the Pawn on f2. If you were in Frazekas's place, playing White, would you resign or find a better solution?

3

INDIAN PROVERB Chess is a sea in which a gnat may drink and an elephant may bathe.

This position is from Tolush-Keres, Leningrad, 1939. Paul Keres, one of the best players of his day, wanted to promote his Black Pawn but was threatened by White playing **1.Qxg7++**. Can you spot the brilliant sequence that Keres found to promote the e-Pawn and deliver mate? Black to move.

4

In this position from Havana, 1965, Boris Ivkov, one of the world's leading Grandmasters, was playing against Gilbero Garcia, a relatively unknown Cuban player. Ivkov is Black and has been winning easily for most of the game. However, his last move, Pawn to d3, was a terrible blunder. How would you, playing White, deliver mate?

5

Here is your chance to checkmate Korchnoi, the famous World Champion contender. This position is from Korchnoi-Karpov in the 1978 World Championship match. Korchnoi has just moved a Rook to a1, one of the worst moves of his career. Can you find how the World Champion, playing Black, mated Korchnoi in just three moves?

World Champions

W. Steinitz (Bohemia/USA)	1886–94
E. Lasker (Germany)	1894–1921
J. Capablanca (Cuba)	1921–27
A. Alekhine (USSR/France)	1927–35
M. Euwe (Holland)	1935–37
A. Alekhine (USSR/France)	1937–46
M. Botvinnik (USSR)	1948–57
V. Smyslov (USSR)	1957–58
M. Botvinnik (USSR)	1958–60
M. Tal (USSR)	1960–61
M. Botvinnik (USSR)	1961–63
T. Petrosian (USSR)	1963–69
B. Spassky (USSR)	1969–72
B. Fischer (USA)	1972–75
A. Karpov (USSR)	1975–85
G. Kasparov (USSR)	1985–

This position is taken from a game between Ståhlberg and Becker, in Buenos Aires, 1944. How would you, playing White, end the game quickly? White to move.

6

Puzzle Master Quest

You have tackled many puzzles and now you should be prepared to face the final challenge – the Puzzle Master Quest. You will encounter six different characters: a Pawn, a Knight, a Bishop, a Rook, a Queen and a King. Each will set you a problem to solve. If you reach the

As you enter the land of the quest, a small figure approaches and you realize it is a foot soldier of the White King.

"You have a puzzle for me?" you ask.

"Of course, of course," says the foot soldier, and he leads you through the trees to a chess board set up with the position shown on the board below.

"White to play and mate in six," says the foot soldier.

"Mate in six?" you exclaim. "That is rather a lot of moves."

The foot soldier just laughs.

"Any Puzzle Master playing White would definitely mate in six moves," he says, and he runs away.

Can you find the right solution and advance one step along your journey?

end of the quest you will be able to call yourself a true Puzzle Master.

Do not worry if you cannot solve all the problems. You become a Puzzle Master not by finding all the answers, but through the knowledge you gain by working on the solutions. Good luck on your quest.

After working on the foot soldier's puzzle, you look around for a place to rest. All of a sudden you hear the sound of snorting and thundering hooves. You look up and see a mighty Knight on horseback.

"Foot soldiers only know silly puzzles," says the Knight disdainfully. "I will show you a real chess problem."

He leads you over a bridge to another chess board set up with the position shown above.

"Now this is a real puzzle," says the Knight proudly. "White, to play, achieves help-mate in four moves."

"You mean that White moves first, and that White and Black then move in such a way that Black mates White on the fourth move?"

"Precisely," says the Knight and rides off, leaving you with the second puzzle on your quest.

Can you see how Black, with White's help, is able to deliver mate in four moves?

Now you are well on your way along the quest and there is no turning back. You walk along the dusty path, wondering what your next problem will be, when you hear a soft, rather shy voice addressing you from behind. You turn around and see a Bishop, dressed in splendid robes and smiling at you gently.

"Knights are so terribly rude," says the Bishop, "and their problems are always so confusing, don't you find?"

"Well," you say, not quite sure what answer is expected of you.

"Have a look at this," says the Bishop, leading you through some gates to a chess board with the position shown below.

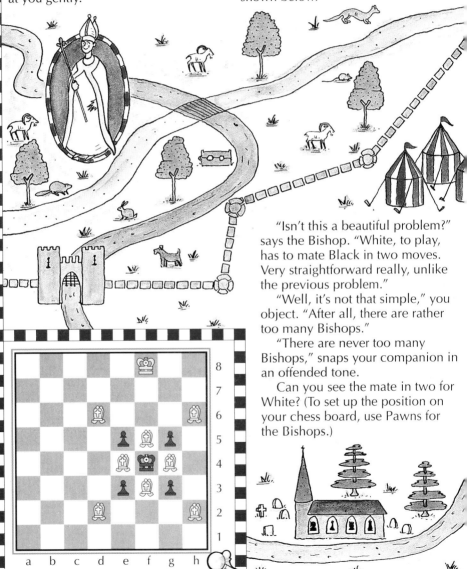

"Isn't this a beautiful problem?" says the Bishop. "White, to play, has to mate Black in two moves. Very straightforward really, unlike the previous problem."

"Well, it's not that simple," you object. "After all, there are rather too many Bishops."

"There are never too many Bishops," snaps your companion in an offended tone.

Can you see the mate in two for White? (To set up the position on your chess board, use Pawns for the Bishops.)

You set off again along the path. As you turn a corner, you are confronted by a majestic castle towering before you. You sigh with awe and your wonder grows as you hear a voice from behind the battlements.

"The Rook is a stately piece and it is now time for a majestic puzzle," booms the voice.

The next moment the drawbridge is lowered and two soldiers dash out. They arrange the position shown on the board above and quickly retreat.

A moment later you hear the resounding voice again.

"In this position, White, to play, is able to mate Black in three moves. But that is not all. White has a choice of three different first moves, all of which lead to mate in three. Think hard and try to find all three solutions."

With that, the drawbridge is raised and you are left alone with your task: to find three different three-move mates for White. Can you discover all three mates?

Your quest is going well but you now have to face the Queen, who is renowned for her perverse and dominating ways. Indeed, your heart sinks as she strides purposefully towards you and presents you with an empty chess board.

"Your task," says the Queen, "is to take eight Queens of the same colour and place them on the chess board in such a way that none of them controls a square that is occupied by another."

"You mean I have to put each of the Queens on a square that is not attacked by the seven other Queens?"

"Precisely," says the Queen. "I should warn you that there is no unique solution. There are many ways in which you may solve the task, but you need find only one of them." (For the eight Queens, use the Pawns from your chess set.)

You are almost there! In the distance you can see the King approaching, smiling confidently, a crown on his head and a sceptre in his hand. With great dignity, the King sets up the position shown below and together you study the arrangement of the pieces on the board.

"An interesting position, don't you think?" says the King.

"Yes, certainly," you reply, not quite sure what to make of it.

"And you notice, of course, that Black has no King?"

"Yes, clearly, Black has no King," you nod.

"Very well," says the King. "You must place the Black King on the board, so that White, to play, is able to deliver mate in three moves."

The King turns and strides off across the lawns and you are left with the final puzzle in your Master Quest.

Puzzle Master

Clues

Page 70   Bishop puzzles

4. Which pieces are exposed when the Black King moves out of check?

Page 71   Rook puzzles

2. To catch the Knight, try attacking the King.

4. Note that the Pawn on a3 is pinned to the King so it cannot guard square b4.

Page 73   King puzzles

3. What has White not yet done on this board?

Pages 74-75   Checkmate in one

2. The mating net around the Black King is nearly complete. Which White piece can move in to deliver mate?

3. Black's mate is quite simple, but for White, remember, it is sometimes best to underpromote a Pawn.

5. Which White piece can take a piece and check the King – without being taken itself?

7. Sometimes it is best to promote a Pawn to a piece other than a Queen.

8. White should have played **1.e4** to give the White King an escape square.

Pages 76-77   Two-move mates

2. Note that the h7 Pawn cannot move as it is defending the King from attack by the h1 Rook.

3. On this board there is no need to put the King in check on the first move.

5. Try using the White g-Pawn to help trap the enemy King.

7. White has lost control of the h1–a8 diagonal because the *fianchettoed* Bishop has been captured. This leaves the g2 square rather vulnerable.

8. White's King is well placed and the Pawns on f2 and g2 cover the Black King's escape squares. Can you spot a move for the White Knight that will ensure checkmate on the following move?

Pages 78-79   More two-movers

1. Black to move. Look for a powerful Black sacrifice that removes the Pawn on g2 and allows the b1 Bishop to mate the White King from square e4

2. Black to move. The Black Bishop on d5 has a powerful mating threat. Can you spot it?

3. Black to move. White cannot force mate in two, but Black has a powerful Queen move.

4. This is a tricky one. It could be Black, but then again, it might be White.

First you need to study the position of each King and try to decide which side is in a position to deliver mate. Black's King is vulnerable because it is almost surrounded by Pawns – the only move for the King is **1...Kxe4**. Can White block this move and so trap the King and then deliver mate?

On the other hand, White's King is also in an awkward position. The only move for the King is **1.Kxe8**, which would expose it to a Rook check from h8. White's only other move is **1.d3**. If Black could block this move, Black might be able to mate the White King. So who is winning – Black or White?

5. Black has two strong Knight moves and, since White is threatening mate, Black must start with a check.

Pages 80-81   Tactics and combinations

1. Black's King and Rooks are vulnerable as they are all on black squares and can be attacked by White's black-squared Bishop. Also, the Black King and d6 Rook can be forked by the e5 Pawn. Can you see how White can sacrifice a Pawn to win an important Black piece with a skewer?

2. Although Black's Queen is pinned to the King, it can still move as long as it does not expose the King. Note also that three of White's pieces – the King, Queen and Bishop – are vulnerable to a skewer attack.

3. If Black moves the Knight on f6, the Black Queen can move down from the back rank to attack.

4. Imagine there were no White Pawn on f2. The Black Queen could then move to h4 and deliver mate. Can you think of a useful Knight move which would enable you to put this idea into practice?

5. Note that the Black King and Queen are on the same diagonal and open to fork attacks.

6. One way to protect the Pawn so it can reach the Queening square is to block the e-file. Can you see how Black can sacrifice a piece to block the file so the Pawn is protected from the Rook's firepower?

7. White cannot stop the threat to the Pawn from the Black Rook but it may be to White's advantage for Black to take this Pawn, for then the Black Rook and King will be on the same rank…

Pages 82-83   Sacrifice to win

3. White's best attacking piece is the Queen, but it is pinned to the King. Which piece can White sacrifice to free the Queen?

5. At present the King has two escape squares – d2 and d4. Can you find a way to bring the King out and trap it in a mating net?

6. The White Knight is blocking the Rook's line of attack. Can you find a move for the Knight that will weaken Black's defences and open the lines for the White Rook?

8. At first glance, the Black King seems well defended by Pawns. But the f7 Pawn is pinned by the White Bishop on b3, the h7 Pawn is blocking the h-file so the White Rook cannot deliver mate, and the g6 Pawn is attacked by the mighty Queen on b1.

Pages 84-85   Study puzzles

1. How can White make the two Bishops work together to complete the mating net around the King? It is important to control escape squares g7 and h8.

2. To deliver mate, not only does White need to leave the a2 Rook where it is, but White also has to move the c8 Rook to a square that is controlled by Black. This is an example of how a study may involve unusual moves.

3. Can you find a way for the b3 Bishop to attack square d7 and complete the mating net around the King?

5. In this puzzle, giving check will not help. You need to move the Queen to increase her firepower. Hint: Try moving back to where you started.

6. Again, a Queen move is required, but this time you must give a check. Do not play **1.Qd3**, though – that was the mistake Norwood made!

Pages 86-87   Save yourself puzzles

1. You have to sacrifice the Queen and then find a way to give perpetual check with the Knight.

2a). Only one of the White pieces can move. With this piece, White can force a draw using either perpetual check or stalemate.

3. Of the two ways to draw, perpetual check and stalemate, perpetual check is clearly impossible as Black has no pieces with which to check the enemy King.

For stalemate, Black must have no legal moves, in other words, both the Black King and the h-Pawn must be blocked. To achieve this, you need to find a way for Black to trap the King with the h-Pawn and the h-Pawn with the King.

Pages 88-89   Advanced winning techniques

1. The first thing to notice on this board is that Black is threatening to win at once with **1…Qxg2++**. There is nothing White can do against this mating threat: **1.g3, Qg2++**; or **1.Kf1, Qxf2++**; or **1.Bf1, Rxg2+; 2.Bxg2, Qxg2++**; or even **1.Be4, Rxg2+; 2.Kh1, Rg4+** discovered check from the Queen on f3; **3.Bxf3, Bxf3++**.

Since you know that Black can deliver mate, you must make sure Black is kept busy elsewhere by keeping Black in check. Now you know that every single one of White's moves must put Black in check, you should be able to see the start of the combination.

Clues continued over the page.   **105**

Clues continued

Pages 88-89 continued

3. If it were Black's move next, Black would be in stalemate and the game would be a draw. So first you must give Black the chance to move. You can play **1.d6**, or move the White King, but after **1.d6**, the quickest mate is **1...exd6**; **2.Kf7, d5**; **3.e5, d4**; **4.e6, d3**; **5.e7++**. Since your task is to mate in four, not five, you must concentrate on your King.

To which square should the King move? If you choose f7 or f5, then Black's reply **1...e5** stops White's attack momentarily as **2.dxe6** *en passant* is stalemate. The only square for White's King is e5. Now Black can play **1...e6** and White must think again as **2.Kxe6** is stalemate and **2.dxe6** allows the Black King to escape from the back rank with **2...Ke7**.

So White must try something different, such as advancing the d-Pawn, which leaves Black with only one move, **2...cxd6+**. To plan your combination, remember that it is best if each of your moves leaves Black with only one possible reply.

6. You might be tempted to move the Knight on g3 to bring about a discovered check from the Queen, but this would not get you very far. Instead, you should look for ways to make the Black pieces work together. The Rook on b3, for example, is out of play, since it is blocked by the Bishop on e3. In the same way, the Queen on e5 would be threatening to take the Rook on e1 if the Bishop were not blocking its path. So, it is the Bishop that you should move as it hinders your other forces.

Pages 90-91 Help-mate puzzles

3. The Black Knight cannot cover enough squares to mate the enemy King, but as this is a help-mate puzzle, try using the White Rook to help trap its own King.

5. The White King cannot be mated in the middle of the board, so you need to find a mating position, for example, the corner where it is most vulnerable. Also, you can only deliver mate with a King and a Bishop if the enemy King is trapped by one of its own pieces, so the White Bishop will have to block one of its own King's escape squares.

6. One of the most common mates is the back rank mate. For Black to deliver a back rank mate within three moves, you need to cover escape squares f2 and h2 with White pieces and remove the Rooks on d1 and e1.

Pages 92-93 Retro-puzzles

2. Here are some of the conclusions Mrs Black arrived at from studying the board:

a) Black's h7 Pawn has captured a piece on g6 and it is the only Black Pawn to have moved.
b) White's h-Pawn may have moved, and it has definitely disappeared. None of the other White Pawns has moved.
c) The White piece taken on g6 cannot have been the h-Pawn. In order to get on to the g-file the White Pawn would have had to have made a capture and Black has not lost any pieces.
d) The only White pieces that could have reached g6 are the h1 Rook and the b1 and g1 Knights, but White is a Pawn down – not a Rook or a Knight. So, and this was Mrs Black's real breakthrough, White must have promoted the h-Pawn to a Rook or Knight.

One last hint – the Rook on h1 need not be the one that started the game on that square. Remember, in retro-puzzles, things are not always as they seem.

Pages 94-95 Brainteasers

1. When you place the Kings on the board there is no reason why the White King should not be in check. It could even be placed right next to the Queen for instance…

3. In fact, every single White move puts Black in check, but for just one of the moves, Black can defend against the check. Can you find a move for White that unpins the Black Rook on b7 so Black can defend the King?

4. It seems impossible for the g1 and g8 Knights to have captured each other in just four moves, and the catch is – they did not! This is a retro-puzzle and in retro-puzzles you should not be taken in by appearances. Can you be sure that the Black Knight on b8 is the one that started the game on that square?

Pages 96-97 Mate the Grandmaster

2. White's position is not as hopeless as it looks. First, to avoid instant defeat, White must give check with the Rook. The Black King moves to apparent safety on h7. Now you need to keep the King in check, perhaps by making a sacrifice, and to use the strength of the Bishop along the a1–h8 diagonal to support one of your most powerful pieces.

3. Black must keep White in check so that White has no chance to deliver mate. It would be worth a grand sacrifice to achieve this objective.

6. The Pawn on g2 is pinned to the White King. It would be worth the greatest sacrifice to tempt the Black Rook away from this pin.

Page 99 Puzzle Master Quest

Remember that this is a help-mate puzzle and the easiest place to checkmate the King is in the corner. A King and Knight cannot mate a lone King, so you need to use the White Knight to help form a mating net by placing it next to its own King. Now you know where the White pieces are placed, you should be able to deduce the mating positions for the Black pieces. A further clue is that each piece has to move twice.

Quest page 100

The Bishop has set a difficult puzzle. At first sight the position seems symmetrical, but when there are Pawns on the board, such symmetry is a decoy, as Pawns can only move forwards. This should tell you which end of the board to study. Also, since the two Bishops on the right are at the edge of the board, they are not as powerful as the Bishops on d2 and d6. This is a clue to which side of the board you should work on.

Now try thinking about Black's responses to White's first move. Whichever piece White moves, Black can move only the Pawn on e3 or g3. See if you can follow this idea through, remembering that Bishops have more firepower on open lines away from the edge of the board.

Quest page 101

In most puzzles where the King and Rook are on their starting squares, the solution involves castling. In this puzzle, however, none of the solutions involve castling.

The neatest solution involves a sacrifice to lure the King to the side of the board where it will be easier to deliver mate. It should not be too difficult to spot which Rook to sacrifice. You then need to bring the White King forward to force the Black King into the mating net.

To help you find the other solutions, note that White, to play, can capture the Pawn with either Rook. Two further clues are that Black is mated on either e3 or g1, and the White King does not move.

Like the Bishop's puzzle, this position appears symmetrical, this time along the e1–h4 diagonal. In fact, the solutions, depending on which Rook takes the Pawn, are reflections of each other. If you work out the solution for one Rook, then hold a mirror near the board, parallel to the e1–h4 diagonal, you should spot how the King is mated when the other Rook takes the Pawn.

Quest page 102

There are many possible solutions to this problem, so you are not looking for one particular position. To approach the solution logically, however, think about how the Queen moves. It can move in the same way as every piece on the board except the Knight. The best way to place the Queens so they do not control the same squares, is Knight-moves away from each other.

Quest page 103

The best place to mate the King is in a corner, or near an edge of the board. Since all the White pieces are still on their starting squares, however, a corner would be too far away for a mate in three. So this should give you a general idea of where the King is placed.

Next, you need to decide whether it is easier to mate on the Kingside or the Queenside. White's first move, which is **1.d4**, should give you a clue.

Answers

Page 68   Pawn puzzles

1. Black can play **1...e1**, promote the Pawn to a Queen or Rook, and checkmate the White King, which is trapped by its own Pawns.

2. **1.fxe5+** captures the Knight – a more valuable piece than the Pawn on g5.

3. **1.gxh3** is the best move because the Black Pawn on h3 is close to promoting.

4. White can play **1.h6**. When Black replies **1...gxh6**, the g-rank is open and the g-Pawn can advance to the promoting square.

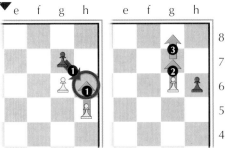

Page 69   Knight puzzles

1. **1.Nxf6+** is the best move since it takes the Rook – a valuable piece.

2. **1.Nxg4+**. This move wins a Pawn and forks the King and Rook. The Black King has to move out of check, so the Knight can take the Rook next move.

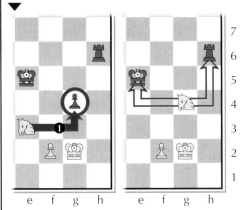

3. **1.Nb6+**. When a Knight checks the enemy King, the opponent has to move the King or capture the Knight. The Knight can hop over pieces, so the King cannot be defended by moving a piece between the Knight and King.

Here, the King is blocked in by a Pawn and the Queen, and White's Bishop is attacking b8. Black's only option is to play **1...Qxb6**. White can then take the Queen with **2.cxb6**.

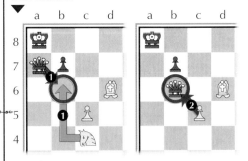

4. Both **1...Nb3** and **1...Nc2** are mate. Note how, by moving the Knight, Black unleashes the power of the Bishop. White is in double check and mate.

Page 70 Bishop puzzles

1. **1.Bb2++**. To checkmate with a King and two Bishops against a King, you need to trap the King in the corner.

2. Black should play **1...Bc8**, so the Bishop covers the critical a6–c8 diagonal and stops any of White's Pawns from advancing.

3. **1...Be2+** forks the King and Knight. When the King moves, Black can take the Knight. This is better than **1...Bxh5**, winning only the h-Pawn.

▼

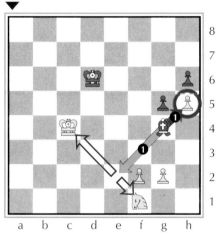

4. **1.Bh3+** is the best move as it skewers the Black Queen. When the King moves, the Queen will be captured. **1.Bd3+** would skewer the Rook – a less valuable piece.

▼

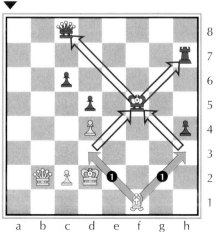

Page 71 Rook puzzles

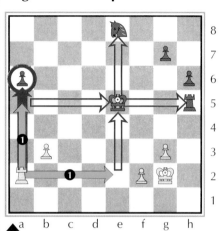

1. The best move is **1.Ra5+**, which will capture the Rook on h5 after the King moves. **1.Rxa6** wins only a Pawn and **1.Re2+** captures the e8 Knight with a skewer attack.

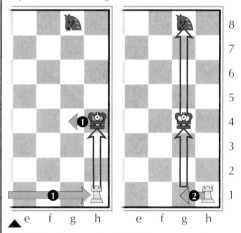

2. **1.Rh1+** forces the Black King on to the g-file so that, after **2.Rg1+**, the Rook will win the Knight on g8 with a skewer attack.

3. **1...Rh1++**.

4. Black can play **1...Rb4+**, forking the King and Knight and taking the Knight next turn. The a3 Pawn cannot take the Rook as it is pinned to the King by the Rook on a1. Nor can the White King take the Rook as the b4 square is attacked by the Pawn on c5.

109

Answers continued

Page 72   Queen puzzles

1. **1.Qg7++**. Note that if White plays **1.Qa8+**, Black blocks with **1...Bf8** and the game continues.

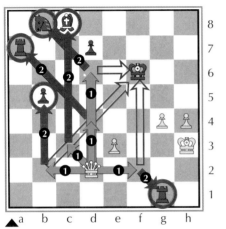

2. The Queen has the five checking moves shown on the board above. **1.Qf2+** wins the Rook on g1. **1.Qd4+** wins the Rook on a7. **1.Qd6+** wins the Knight on b8 and **1.Qc3+** wins the Bishop on c8. **1.Qb2+** wins the Pawn on b5. Such is the power of the Queen.

4. **1...Qb8++**. Note that the advancing Pawns are unable to help. The Pawn on a7 cannot take the Queen as it is pinned by the a1 Rook.

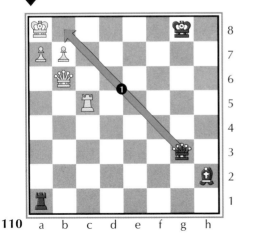

3. Avoid the disastrous **1.Qh1+**, followed by **2.Qxb7**, capturing the Rook when the King moves. Black can play **2...Ne3+**, forking the White King and Queen, as shown below. Safer is **1.Qe5+** (shown at the bottom) or **1.Qe1+**, **Kd5**; **2.Qe5+**, winning the Knight on e6 with a fork attack.

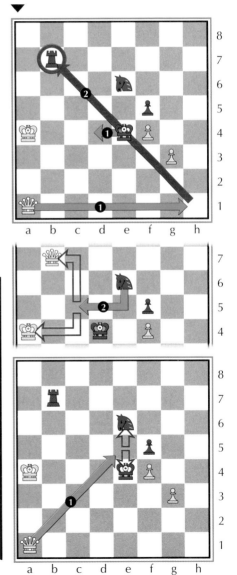

Page 73   King puzzles

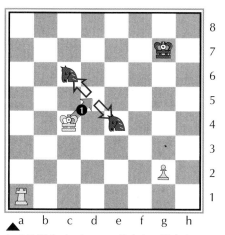

1. **1.Kd5** forks the two Knights. This is an unusual role reversal that wins White a Knight. Usually it is the Knight which carries out a fork.

2. **1...Kc7++**. The White King is trapped in the corner and mated by a discovered check from the Bishop.

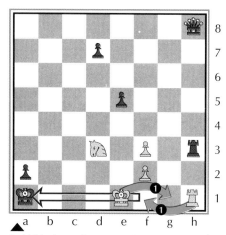

3. White's mating move is **1.0-0++**. In this example, White was wise not to castle too early in the game.

4. **1.Kf4** is the way to *zugzwang* Black, that is, put Black in a position where every move will lead to disaster. Black's only move is **1...g3**. White can then play **2.hxg3++**.

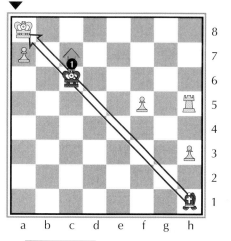

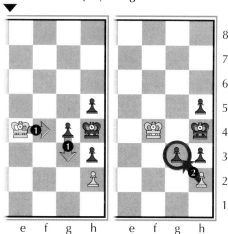

Pages 74-75 Checkmate in one

1. The winning move is **1.Bf6++**. In the actual game, Grandmaster Svetozar Gligorić of Yugoslavia played **1.Rd1+** and just managed to win after 19 more moves.

2. The Grandmaster played **1.Re5++**, as shown in the diagram on the right. ▶

3. Black can play **1...Rh6++**. White can mate with **1.dxc8(N)++**, underpromoting the Pawn to a Knight.

4. **1.Bd8++**. This stops the King escaping to b6. When looking for checkmate, always remember to cut off every one of the King's escape squares.

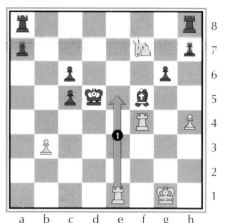

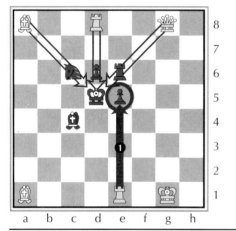

◀ 5. **1.Rxe5++**. None of Black's pieces can take the Rook – they are all pinned to the King, as shown in the diagram on the left.

6. **1...Bd3++**, double check and mate from the Bishop and Rook. If, instead, the Bishop moved to h3, the King could still escape to e2. ▼

◀ 7. White can play **1.f8(N)++**, underpromoting to a Knight as shown in the two pictures on the left. This mates the King by enabling the h7 Rook to defend the e7 Pawn, and allowing the Bishop on h5 to cover square e8.

8. Black played **1...Nd3++**. The Pawn on e2 is pinned by the Black Queen so the White King is trapped in a smothered mate.

Pages 76-77   Two-move mates

1. **1...Nh3+** forces White to play **2.Kh1**. Black can then play **2...Bb7++**. To mate with a King, Bishop and Knight against a lone King, you need to force the enemy King on to a corner square of the same colour as the diagonals along which your Bishop can move.

2. After **1.Ne7+**, Black can play only **1...Kh8**. Now White can play **2.Nfxg6++** (shown on the right). Did you see that Black's Pawn on h7 cannot take the Knight as it is pinned to the King by the White Rook on h1?

3. **1.Rh1** is the winning move. White is not checking the enemy King but there is no way Black can avoid White's next move: **2.Kg1++**.

4. Black can play **1...Nf3+**, shielding the King from check and at the same time, checking White so that White's next move, **2.Kh1** is forced. Black can now play **2...Rxh2++**. Note that White's Queen is pinned by the Rook on a1 and cannot capture the Knight.

5. White can win with **1.g5+**. If Black takes the Pawn with **1...Kxg5**, then White can play **2.Qf4++** (see right). Alternatively, if Black plays **1...Bxg5**, then White can play **2.Qg7++** or **2.Rh8++** (far right). In the actual game, Grandmaster Samuel Reshevsky played **1.Qxg6+** and lost his Queen.

6. The only way to mate is **1.Rg8+**, and discovered check from the c3 Bishop. The Black King now has to take the Rook with **1...Kxg8** and White wins with **2.Rg1++**.

7. If Black plays **1...Bh3**, White, having no Bishop to control the squares around the King, cannot prevent **2...Qg2++**. Making the Queen and Bishop work together like this is one of the most common ways of mating the enemy King, especially when your opponent has no Bishop to control the diagonal.

8. White can win with **1.Ng1**. White now has two mating threats: **2.g3+** and **2.Nf3+** (shown on the right). Black can only tackle one threat at a time. If Black plays **1...Bc7** to stop White from playing **2.g3**, then White wins with **2.Nf3++**. If Black plays **1...g4** to prevent **2.Nf3**, then White wins with **2.g3++**.

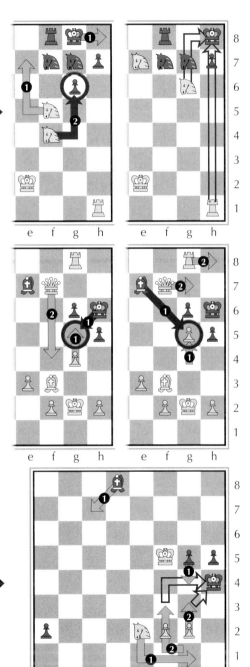

Pages 78-79 More two-movers

1. Black can win by sacrificing the Rook with ▶
1...Rxh3+; **2.gxh3**, **Be4++** as shown on the
right.

2. It is in fact Black who can force mate. After
1...f6, Black threatens **2...Bf7++**. If White
plays **2.g5** to give the King an escape square,
then Black wins with **2...Bf3++**.

3. Again, it is Black who can mate in two.
After **1...Qf1**, whatever White plays, Black
will reply with **2...Qg2++**.

4. The winning move is **d3** and the trick is
that either side can win with this move. If
White plays first (**1.d3**), Black cannot prevent
White playing **2.Bf4++**, as shown below.

▼　　　　　*Solution continued below right.*

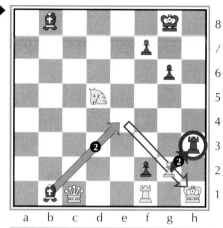

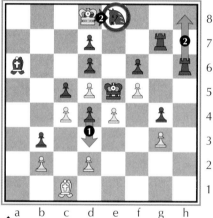

If Black plays **1...d3** (shown above), White's
only move is **2.Kxe8**, as all the White Pawns
are blocked. Black now wins with **2...Rh8++**.

◀ 5. Black can win with **1...Nf3+** or **1...Nh3+**
(shown left). After **1...Nf3+**, White is forced to
play **2.Kh1** and is mated by **2...Qxh2++**. If
Black plays **1...Nh3+**, White again has to play
2.Kh1 and Black wins with **2...Bxg2++**.

6. White can play **1.Ba7+**, forcing Black to
move **1...Ka8**. White can then play **2.Qc8++**.
Alternatively, White can win by sacrificing
the Rook as follows: **1.Ra8+**, **Kxa8**; **2.Qc8++**.
Both methods win by forcing the King into the
corner so the Queen can attack in safety.

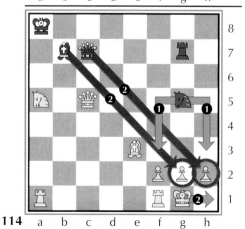

Pages 80-81 Tactics and combinations

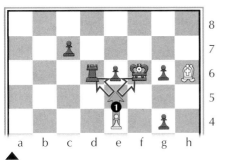

1. **1.e5+** forks the King and d6 Rook (shown above). Black can either move the King and lose the Rook, or play **1...Kxe5**. White can then skewer the King and a1 Rook with **2.Bg7+**, winning the Rook when the King moves (shown right). If White skewered the d6 Rook with **2.Bf4**, followed by **3.Bxd6**, then Black could take the Bishop with the c7 Pawn.

2. Black can play the crushing combination **1...Qxb4+**; **2.Kxb4, Ra4+**. After White's King moves away, Black takes the Queen on g4.

3. Black can play **1...Nxe4**. After White recaptures with either **2.fxe4** or **2.Nxe4**, Black can play **2...Qh4+**, checking the White King and forking the White Bishop on h6, which can be taken next move.

4. Black can play **1...Ne3**. White's Queen is attacked and cannot move away. If White takes the Knight with **2.fxe3**, then Black can win the game with **2...Qh4+**; **3.g3, Qxg3++**.

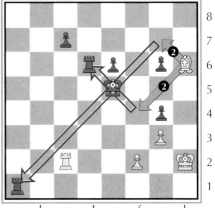

5. White should play **1.Bc5+**, sacrificing the Bishop in a fork attack on the Black King and Queen. After **1...Qxc5**, White can play **2.Ne6+**, this time forking the King and Queen with the Knight, and taking the Queen next move after the King has moved away.

6. Black's winning move is **1...Be6+**, forking the King and Rook. White is forced to play **2.Kxe6** and now the White King shields Black's Pawn from attack by the Rook, and Black can promote the Pawn.

7. White should play **1.Rh8**, threatening to promote the a-Pawn. If Black replies with **1...Rxa7**, White can play **2.Rh7+**, a skewer attack on the King and Rook that wins the Rook next turn.

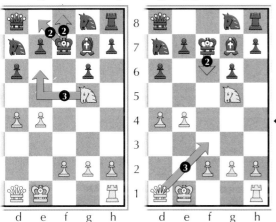

8. White's best move would have been **1.Bxf7+**. If Black plays **1...Kf8**, he remains a Pawn down and if he plays **1...Kxf7**, he has to put up with **2.Ng5+**. After this Knight check, Black can make three different moves, all of which are disastrous for Black, as shown in the diagrams on the left.

If Black plays **2...Kf8** or **2...Ke8**, as shown far left, then **3.Ne6** wins the Queen on d8 (the pieces are shown after White's second move). Alternatively, if Black decides to try **2...Kf6**, as shown on the left, then White wins the game with **3.Qf3++**.

115

Pages 82-83 Sacrifice to win

1. White can play **1.Qg7+**, sacrificing the Queen to the Knight when Black replies with **1...Nxg7**. Now the Black King is trapped in a cage of its own pieces and White can use the Knight to hop in and deliver smothered mate with **2.Nf6++**.

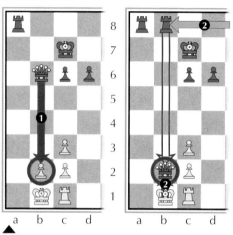

7. White should sacrifice the Queen with **1.Qg8+**. After **1...Rxg8**, White wins with **2.Nf7++**.

8. Again, White should sacrifice the Queen. After **1.Qxg6+**, Black cannot move the King, nor can the Queen be taken by the f-Pawn as it is pinned by the Bishop on b3, as shown below. Black has no choice but **1...hxg6**, after which White wins with **2.Rh8++**.

2. Black can win by sacrificing the Queen: **1...Qxb2+**; **2.Kxb2, Rgb8++**, as shown in the diagrams above. When the enemy King is defended by only a thin line of Pawns, the attacking side should try to break it up. Often the only way to do this is with a sacrifice.

3. To release the Queen from the Rook pin, White should play **1.Rd8+**. Black has to take the Rook with **1...Rxd8**. White can then deal the final blow with **2.Qxa7++**.

4. Norwood played **1.Rxa7+**. Black had to take the Rook with **1...Kxa7**, and White could then mate with **2.Qa5++**. Did you notice that the Black Queen is pinned to the King by the White Queen and so cannot take the Rook?

5. The only way for Black to achieve checkmate is **1...Bb4+**; **2.Kxb4, Qa5++**. As in Puzzle 1, sacrificing a piece helps to trap the enemy King in a cage of its own pieces.

6. White is lucky to have the forcing combination **1.Nb6+**, to which Black has to reply **1...axb6** so White can win with **2.Ra4++**.

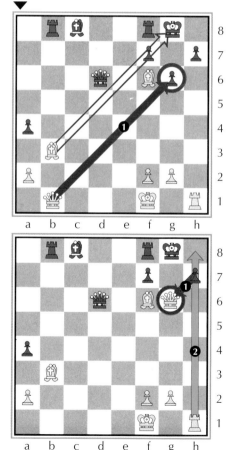

Pages 84-85 Study puzzles

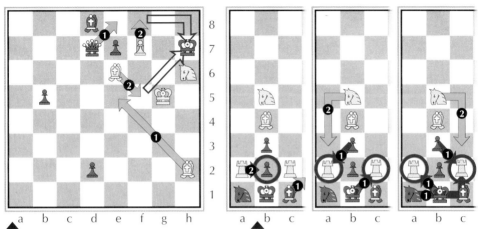

a b c d e f g h

▲
1. To give mate, White can play **1.Be5**. This leaves the Black King trapped, since White threatens checkmate by underpromoting the Pawn on f8 to a Knight with **2.f8(N)++** (see above). The only defence is **1...Qe8**, but then **2.Bf5++** is an alternative mate.

3. White's move is **1.Ba4.** It may seem crazy to move the Bishop from the same diagonal as the Black King, but an unusual move like this is often the key to the study. From a4, the Bishop covers square d7 and completes the mating net around the Black King, shown on the right. If Black captures the Knight that is now unprotected on d5, then the Bishop returns to b3 to give mate. If Black plays **1...d6**, White wins with **2.Nbc7++**. Other possibilities are **1...e4; 2.Qxe4++**, or **1...f5; 2.Qg8++**, or **1...f6; 2.Ndc7++**.

4. **1.Kg8** completes the mating net around the Black King, so mate is inevitable: **1...Qxg5+; 2.Bg7++** discovered check and mate from the Queen on b6, for example, or **1...Rxf6; 2.Qxf6++**. Or, if Black plays **1...Qb1** (to stop **2.Rh7++**), then White plays **2.Nf7++**.

5. **1.Qd1** leaves Black in *zugzwang*. If Black plays **1...Kd3**, then **2.Rxd5++**. If **1...Kc5**, **2.Qg1** is mate since the d5 Pawn is pinned to the King by the Rook on e5 and is not able to block the check. Capturing the Rook with **1...Kxe5** provokes **2.d4++**.

2. **1.Rc2** will mate Black next move. If Black moves the c1 Bishop, then White mates with **2.Raxb2++** (above left). If Black plays **1...Kxc2** or **1...bxa2**, White mates with **2.Na3++** (centre). If Black plays **1...Kxa2**, **1...Nxc2**, or **1...bxc2**, White mates with **2.Nc3++** (right).

▲

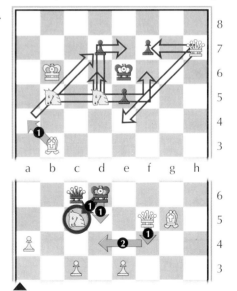

a b c d e f g h

▲
6. Our author should have played **1.Qf4+**. The Black King can then capture the Knight on c5 or move to d5, as shown above. Either way, **2.Qd4++** leaves Black in checkmate.

117

Pages 86-87   Save yourself puzzles

1. White draws by sacrificing the Queen and then causing perpetual check: **1.Qxf8+**, **Nxf8**; **2.Nf7+**, **Kg8** (see below left); **3.Nh6+**, **Kh8**. **4.Nf7+** and so on, as shown below right. The Black King is trapped on squares g8 and h8 and cannot escape from check as the White Knight hops between f7 and h6.

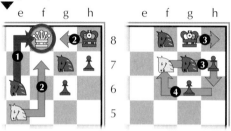

2a) The only piece White can move is the Rook. The Pawns are blocked and the White King cannot move. If White plays **1.Rg8+** and Black takes the Rook with **1...Kxg8**, the game ends in stalemate as White has no other pieces that can move.

If, however, the Black King tries to escape from the White Rook, the game ends in a draw as follows: **1...Kh7**; **2.Rg7+**, **Kh6**; **3.Rh6+**, **Kh5**; **4.Rg5+**, **Kh4** (**4...Bxg5** is stalemate); **5.Rh4+** perpetual check.

b) Without the Pawn on e5, the Black Queen can defend square g7 and White will lose as shown below: **1.Rg8+**, **Kh7**; **2.Rg7+**, **Qxg7**; **3.Kc1** (White's only move), **Qb2++**.

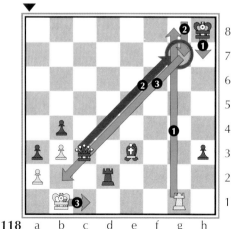

3. Black has an ingenious series of moves that leads to stalemate: **1...Kg6** (or **Kh6** – it makes no difference); **2.a5**, **Kh5**; **3.a6**, **Kh4**; **4.a7**, **h5**; **5.a8(Q)** and Black has no legal moves left. Note that there is nothing White can do about Black's manoeuvre.

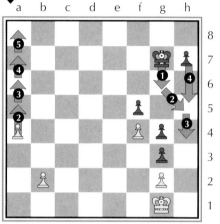

4. White can either win or force a draw, whichever piece Black chooses for the Pawn.

a) Pawn to Knight – White wins with **2.Qd1++**.

b) Pawn to Bishop – White can again win with **2.Qd1++**.

c) Pawn to Rook – White can force a draw with **2.Qb5+**, **Qxb5** and the game ends in stalemate as White has no legal move.

d) Pawn to Queen – White can force a draw with **2.Qd1+**, **Qxd1**, again ending the game in stalemate with no legal move for White. Note that **2.Qb5+** does not work because Black is not compelled to capture the Queen and can play a move such as **2...Kc2**, leaving Black a Queen up and guaranteeing a win for Black.

DID YOU KNOW? Napoleon was a keen but mediocre chess player. After making himself emperor, however, he rarely lost a game as hardly anyone dared to beat him.

Pages 88-89   Advanced winning techniques*

1. The winning combination is **1.Qxd7+, Kxd7**; **2.Bf5+** (double check from the Rook and Bishop), **Ke8**; **3.Bd7+, Kf8**; **4.Bxe7++** (or **2...Kc6**; **3.Bd7++**). Note how White uses some common attacking ideas, first sacrificing the Queen to draw out the King and put Black in check, then playing double check, which forces Black's King to move so White can play two powerful Bishop checks and deliver mate.

2. If White plays **1.Qh6**, Black has no escape. White threatens to play **2.Qxg7++** and if Black tries to defend with **1...Bxh6**, White can reply with **2.Ne7++**. If, on the other hand, Black takes the Bishop with **1...Bxf6**, White wins with **2.Nxf6+, Qxf6** (or **2...Kh8**; **3.Qxh7++**); **3.exf6** and whatever Black replies, White can play **4.Qg7++**.

3. White's winning combination is ingenious – every single move White plays leaves Black with only one possible reply: **1.Ke5, e6**; **2.d6, cxd6**; **3.Kxd6, e5**; **4.c7++**. Although White's main problem is to avoid stalemating Black, the fact that Black has so few replies means that White can control Black's moves.

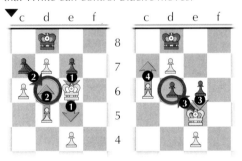

4. The winning combination is **1.Rg4+, fxg4**; **2.Qg5+, Kh8**; **3.Qh6**, and now Black is lost for moves. If Black tries to defend the Rook on f8 with **3...Qd8** or **3...Raa8**, then White wins with **4.Qxh7++**. If Black tries to avoid the mate on h7 with **3...f5** or **3...Bxd3**, then White wins with **4.Qxf8++**. Note how the sacrifice of the White Rook on g4 unleashes the Bishop's power by opening up the b1–h7 diagonal, and how the White Queen moves from f6 to g5 to h6 to bring about a double threat that wins on f8 or h7.

5. White can win with **1.Qxa7+, Kxa7** (reaching the position shown below left); **2.Ra2+, Qa4**; **3.Rxa4++**. White sacrifices the Queen to draw out the King. This leaves the King unprotected on the a-file, and cut off from the b-file by the White Rooks, as shown below right.

▼

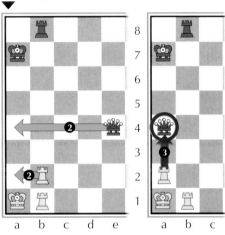

6. The winning move is **1...Bg1+**, a Bishop sacrifice. Now, White cannot avoid checkmate. If White takes the Bishop with the King (**2.Kxg1**), Black plays **2...Qxe1+**, followed by **3.Qf1, Qxf1+**; **4.Kh2, Qh1++**. Note how the sacrifice of the Bishop enables the Black Queen to take the Rook on e1 and allows the Knight on g3 to be protected by the Rook on b3.

   If, on the other hand, White takes the Bishop with the Rook on g2 (**2.Rgxg1**), then Black mates as follows: **2...Nf1** double check – the discovered check from the Queen is now very strong as it is supported by the Knight check; **3.Kg2** (or **Kh1** – it makes no difference), **Qh2++**.

   Alternatively, if White takes the Bishop with the Rook on e1 (**2.Rexg1**), then Black mates with **2...Nf1** double check; **3.Kh1, Rxh3+**; **4.Rh2, Rxh2++**.

   Although the Bishop sacrifice looks a little surprising, it allows Black's other pieces to leap into action and it is only when they all work together that White can be mated.

* These answers are quite complicated, so it is a good idea to follow the moves on a chess board.

119

Pages 90-91   Help-mate puzzles

1. **1.Kd1** and Black mates with **1...Rh1++**.

2. White should move **1.Bg1** so Black can play **1...Kg3++** discovered check and mate.

3. **1.Kh1, Nf5; 2.Rh2, Ng3++**. The White King moves into the corner and is then trapped by the White Rook, while the Black Knight hops into battle position ready to deliver mate.

5. **1.Ke4, Kc6; 2.Kf3, Kd5; 3.Kg2, Ke4; 4.Kh1, Kf3; 5.Bh2, Kf2++**. The White King moves to h1, which is more vulnerable than a1 or h8 since it is on the diagonal occupied by the Black Bishop. The White Bishop then moves to h2 to trap the White King and the Black King moves to f2 to unleash the power of the Black Bishop, as shown in the diagram below.

▼

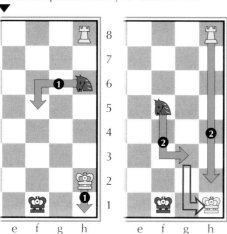

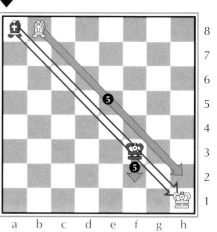

4. Help-mate is brought about with the following moves: **1...Ke7; 2.Kg7, Ke8; 3.Kf6, Kf8; 4.Rh8++**. The Black King stays on a vulnerable square at the edge of the board. The White King moves away from the edge of the board so it can attack more squares and make room for the Rook.

▼

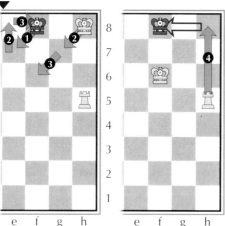

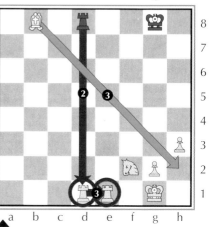

6. White can be mated on the back rank as follows: **1.Nf2, Rd8; 2.b8(B)** (reaching the position shown above), **Rxd1; 3.Bh2, Rxe1++**. The King is trapped by the White Knight and Bishop. Did you see that **2.b8(Q)** is not possible as it pins the Black Rook on d8?

Pages 92-93   Retro-puzzles

1. To find who could have taken the Black Knight, set up the position shown on the board and consider each piece in turn:

The Pawns – Obviously the Black Knight could not have been taken by a Pawn as the White e-Pawn has not moved diagonally for a capture, and none of the other White Pawns have moved at all.

The Knights – Knights can leap out from the back rank, so a White Knight could have taken the Black Knight and then returned to its position.

The King, Queen and captured Bishop – Since the White e-Pawn has advanced two squares, any one of these pieces could have marched out, captured the Knight and then returned to its place.

The Rooks – Even these could have captured the Knight. If both the White King and g-Knight moved, the h1 Rook would be free. Even the a1 Rook could have captured the Knight if, say, the White Knight on b1 had moved out and the Black Knight had moved down to b1 via c6, a5, c4 and a3. Afterwards, the Rook could have returned to a1 and the White Knight to b1. Unlikely, but possible.

The c1 Bishop – No, this piece could not have captured the Knight as it is imprisoned by the b2 and d2 Pawns.

So, the Black Knight could not have been captured by a White Pawn or by the Bishop on c1, but any of the other pieces might have taken it. Working on this kind of puzzle helps you to become aware of all the possible moves leading to even a simple position.

---

2. Mrs Black was right – the h1 Rook has moved and so White is not allowed to castle. The piece captured on g6 must have been a Knight or a Rook and not a Pawn, as the White Pawn could not reach the g-file without making a capture – and Black has not lost any pieces.

Since, however, White is a Pawn and not a Knight or a Rook down, White must have underpromoted the h-Pawn to a Knight or a Rook. White must have chosen to promote to a Rook, because a Knight would have been trapped on h8 as both f7 and g6 are occupied by Black Pawns.

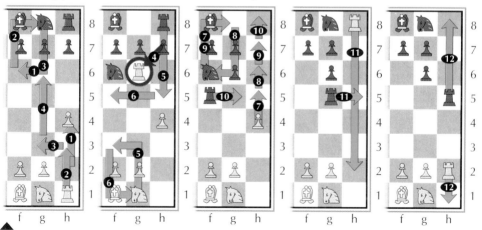

The moves made by the original players are listed here and shown on the five diagrams above: **1.h4**, Nf6; **2.Rh3**, Ng8; **3.Rg3**, Nf6; **4.Rg6** (diagram one), hxg6; **5.Nf3**, Rh5; **6.Ng1**, Rf5 (diagram two); **7.h5**, Ng8; **8.h6**, Nf6; **9.h7**, Ng8; **10.h8(R)**, Rg5 (diagram three); **11.Rh2**, Rh5 (diagram four); **12.Rh1**, Rh8 (diagram five).

Pages 94-95 Brainteasers

1. The White King is on f3. The Black King is in the corner on h1, under fire from the two Bishops. White's mating move is **1 Kxf2++**, a discovered check from the Bishop on d5.

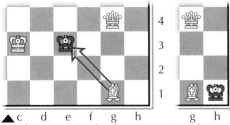

2a) The King is in checkmate on e3 as shown above left. b) The King is in stalemate on h1 (centre). c) The King is on a8 so that, after **1.Qc8**, Black is in checkmate (right).

3. White's move is **1.Rc6+**. On square c6, the White Rook blocks the h1–a8 diagonal and the Black Rook, which was pinned by the a8 Bishop, can now capture the Bishop on h7. This is the only solution to this puzzle – any other move would put Black in checkmate.

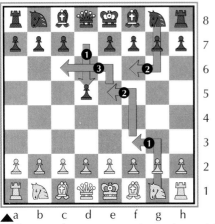

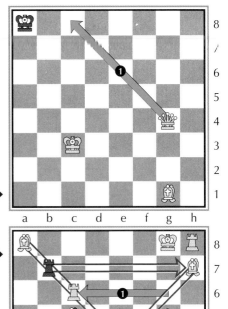

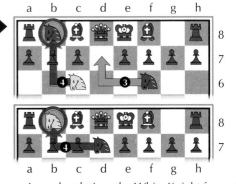

4. There are four ways to arrive at the position shown in the puzzle. For example: **1.Nf3**, **d5**; **2.Ne5**, **Nf6**; **3.Nc6** (shown above), **Nfd7**; **4.Nxb8**, **Nxb8** (shown in the two pictures right). It is the Black Knight on b8 which was captured and not the g8 Knight.

Another solution is: **1.Nf3**, **Nf6**; **2.Nd4**, **d5**; **3.Nc6**, **Nfd7**; **4.Nxb8**, **Nxb8**.

In each solution, the White Knight from g1 has to reach square c6 on its third move and this can be done via f3 and d4 or f3 and e5. The Black Knight on g8 has to reach square d7 on its third move. Black can do this by playing either **1...d5** or **1...Nf6**. As soon as the two Knights are on squares c6 and d7, the double Knight capture can take place.

Pages 96-97 Mate the Grandmaster

1. **1.Qg1+**, **Kd2**; **2.Qc1+**, **Kd3**; **3.Qc3++**, giving the mating position shown below.

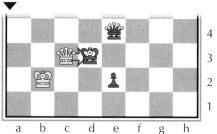

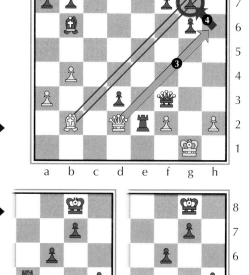

2. White can deliver mate in four as follows: **1.Rc8+**, **Kh7**; **2.Rh8+**, **Kxh8** (giving the position shown on the right); **3.Qh6+**, **Kg8** (the g7 Pawn cannot capture the Queen as it is pinned by the b2 Bishop, as shown in the diagram); **4.Qxg7‖**.

3. **1...Qg3+**; **2.Kxg3**. Keres's sacrifice of the Queen leaves White with no chance to deliver mate. Now, when Keres promotes the Pawn, the King is again in check and he can deliver mate as shown in the two diagrams on the right: **2...e1(Q)+**; **3.Kh3**, **Re3+**; **4.Kh2**, **Qg3+**; **5.Kg1**, **Re1++**. An alternative mate is **3.Kh2**, **Qxh4+**; **4.Kg1**, **Re1++**.

4. Ivkov's Pawn move opened the a1–h8 diagonal. White should play **1.Bc3** to strenghten White's control of the a1–h8 diagonal so Black is unable to prevent the inevitable **2.Qh8++**.

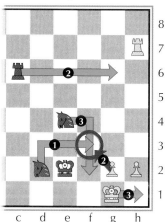

5. Karpov played **1...Nf3+** (sacrificing the Knight to bring out White's Pawn), and the game ended with the following moves: **2.gxf3 Rg6+**; **3.Kh1**, **Nf2++**. An alternative mate would have been **2.Kh1**, **Nf2++**.

6. **1.Qe1+**, **Rxe1**; **2.g3++** as shown on the right. The sacrifice of the Queen frees the g2 Pawn, which was pinned to the King.

123

Page 98   Puzzle Master Quest

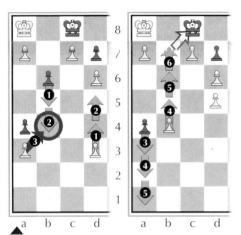

The trick to this puzzle is that the answer is forced. If you are playing White you simply cannot avoid delivering mate since, for each move, both Black and White have only one possible move: **1.d4**, **b5**; **2.d5**, **b4**; **3.axb4** (shown above left), **a3**; **4.b5**, **a2**; **5.b6**, **a1** (above right). Black can promote the a-Pawn but White has checkmate anyway with **6.b7++**. This study is by a man named Ropke, and is dubbed "The easiest problem of all".

Quest page 99

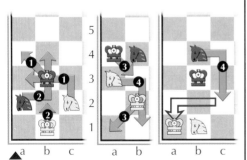

1.Na3, **Ka4**; **2.Kb2** (the White King has to lose a move before heading into the corner, or Black cannot set up the mating net), **Nb4**; **3.Ka1**, **Kb3**; **4.Nb1**, **Nc2++**. This is a classic help-mate puzzle in the sense that the pieces have to be rearranged very carefully to create the mating net for the final position.

Quest page 100

White should play **1.Bc3**. If Black replies **1...e2**, White can play **2.Bd2++**. If, however, Black's first move is **1...gxh2**, as shown below, White can mate with **2.Bxe5++**.

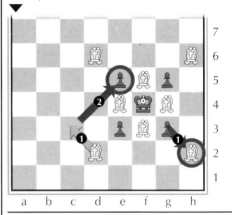

Quest page 101

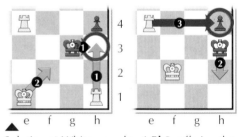

Solution a) White can play **1.Rh3**, offering the Rook. If Black accepts the sacrifice with **1...Kxh3**, then **2.Kf2** forces Black to play **2...Kh2** and White can mate with **3.Rxh4++**.

If Black declines the sacrifice with **1...Kg2** (as shown below), White can play **2.Rexh4**. Black is forced to play **2...Kg1**, and White mates with **3.Rg3++**.

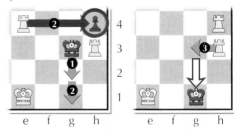

Solution continued opposite.

Quest page 101 continued

Solution b) White can play **1.Rhxh4**. Now
Black has two choices: **1...Kf3** or **1...Kg2**.
If **1...Kf3**, then **2.Reg4**, **Ke3**; **3.Rg3++**.
If **1...Kg2**, then **2.Re3**, **Kg1**; **3.Rg3++**.

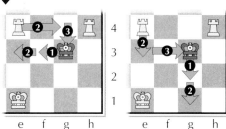

Solution c) After **1.Rexh4**, Black has the same
two choices as above: **1...Kf3** or **1...Kg2**.
If **1...Kf3**, then **2.Rg1**, **Ke3**; **3.Rg3++**.
If **1...Kg2**, then **2.R(h1)h3**, **Kg1**; **4.Rg3++**.

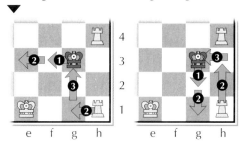

Quest page 102

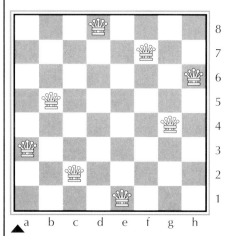

A man called Dr Nauck published all the
solutions for this problem in 1850. His
calculations showed that there were 92
possible variations of the basic theme of
placing the Queens Knight-moves away
from each other. For example, the Queens
can be on a3, b5, c2, d8, e1, f7, g4 and h6.

You may have found a different solution
which is fine, as long as none of the Queens
is on the same rank, file or diagonal as
another Queen.

Quest page 103

The Black King must be on h4. This is the
square to which White can most quickly
develop pieces to trap the King. To deliver
mate, White plays **1.d4**, after which Black has
two choices: **1...Kg4** or **1...Kh5**.

If Black moves **1...Kg4**, then **2.e4+**, **Kh4**;
3.g3++, as shown below left.
If Black moves **1...Kh5**, then **2.Qd3**, **Kg4**
(or **Kh4**); **3.Qh3++**, as shown in the
diagram below.

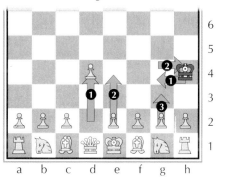

Famous players

In the history of chess, certain players stand out because of their achievements in the game. On these two pages you can read about some of the most famous players of the last 150 years.

Wilhelm Steinitz (17 May 1836 – 12 August 1900) Born: Prague, Czechoslovakia

Steinitz was the first official World Champion and held the title for 28 years, which is longer than any other player. Steinitz was one of the most profound thinkers in chess, although he suffered from insanity when he grew older. He was the first player to challenge the Romantic style of playing chess, which involved dashing attacks against the enemy King. Instead, Steinitz emphasized the importance of defence and positional chess – playing for control of weak squares, for example, and avoiding poor Pawn positions.

In the last few years of his life, Steinitz became completely mad. Chess still dominated his mind, however. He believed he could move chess pieces simply by sending out electrical signals from his brain.

Paul Morphy (22 June 1837 – 10 July 1884) Born: New Orleans, USA

Paul Morphy was already an accomplished chess player before he reached his teens. After defeating all the top American players, he arrived in London, England, on his 21st birthday, intending to challenge Europe's finest Masters.

Morphy alternated between St George's chess club in London and the *Café de la Régence* in Paris and defeated many of the world's leading players. However, the leading English Master, Howard Staunton (after whom the Staunton chess set is named) did everything to avoid playing Morphy. Morphy was disappointed and frustrated because of this, and returned to America in December 1860.

After his return, Morphy grew to detest chess. Like Steinitz, he began to show signs of madness and no one was allowed to mention chess in his presence. Many people believed that Morphy's madness was caused by playing too many games of blindfold chess.

Emanuel Lasker (24 December 1868 – 11 January 1941) Born: Berlinchen, Prussia

Lasker became World Champion in 1894 when he defeated Wilhelm Steinitz. He was one of the first chess players to demand large fees for playing important games, so in that sense, he was one of the first professional chess players. He successfully defended his title against challengers for 27 years, but finally lost to José Raoúl Capablanca in 1921. As well as his achievements in chess, Lasker became a doctor of mathematics and was a philosopher, dramatist and poet. He was also an accomplished card player and was leader of the German team at the Bridge Olympics.

Harry Nelson Pillsbury (5 December 1872 – 17 June 1906) Born: Massachusetts, USA

Although Pillsbury didn't learn the moves of chess until the late age of 16, within a few years he was the best player in America. Like Morphy, he decided to travel to Europe and in 1895 he won the Hastings Tournament in England, the most prestigious tournament of that time.

Pillsbury is remembered for his amazing memory (see *Did you know* page 111). He also operated a mechanical chess player called Ajeeb. People were fooled into believing that the machine worked out the moves for itself, but in fact they were made by the operator hidden inside.

Had Pillsbury not died at the early age of 33, people believe he may have gone on to become World Champion.

José Raoúl Capablanca (19 November 1888 – 8 March 1942) Born: Havana, Cuba

Capablanca learned to play chess at the age of four by watching his father play with a friend. Soon, he took the chess world by storm and between 1916 and 1924, he did not lose a single game. In 1921, he captured the world title by convincingly defeating Emanuel Lasker, and around this time his superiority over other players was so great that he felt that the game was too easy and that its rules should be changed. He was soon to be defeated, however, by the next World Champion, Alexander Alekhine.

Sultan Khan (1905 – 1966)
Born: Punjab, India

Before World War II, most chess Masters came from middle class or upper class families. Sultan Khan was unusual in that he worked as a slave to a diplomat all his life and could neither read nor write. He began playing chess at the age of nine and quickly became one of India's leading players. In 1928, Khan's master brought him to England and within a year he became British Champion. This was a particularly impressive achievement since the rules of chess in Europe differed from the Indian rules. Sultan Khan's international career was brought to an abrupt end when his master took him back to India in 1933. The chess world never heard of him again.

Robert James Fischer (9 March 1943 –)
Born: Chicago, USA

Robert (better known as Bobby) Fischer is the best known chess player of all time. Many people believe he is also the most capable player of all time. One of his most stunning feats was to win 19 consecutive games against top Grandmasters.

Fischer did more than any other player to increase people's interest in chess. He became well known for his strong personality and regularly created world headlines. He would often accuse the Soviet players of cheating and was constantly threatening to pull out of games.

In 1972, millions of televisions viewers worldwide watched Fischer's brilliant victory over Boris Spassky in the final of the World Championship in Reykjavic, Iceland. Since he beat Spassky, however, Fischer has refused to play another game of chess – even to defend his title in the 1975 World Championship. The title went instead to the Soviet player, Anatoly Karpov and has stayed with the Soviets ever since. Bobby Fischer now lives as a recluse somewhere in America.

Garry Kimovich Kasparov (13 April 1963 –)
Born: Baku, USSR

Kasparov became the youngest ever World Champion when he defeated Karpov in Moscow in 1985. He was 22 years old. Since then, he has successfully defended his title against Karpov three times and finished first in nearly every tournament that he has competed in. In 1990, he achieved a rating of 2800 on the FIDE rating system (the international chess ranking system). This is the highest ever rating (Bobby Fischer achieved the next highest rating of 2785).

Outside the world of chess, Kasparov has an active interest in Soviet politics. He has even considered forming his own political party.

Judit Polgar (23 July 1976 –)
Born: Budapest, Hungary

Judit Polgar has proved many critics wrong by showing that you do not have to be male to be an outstanding chess player. For over 30 years, Bobby Fischer held the record as the youngest ever chess Grandmaster. In 1992, Judit Polgar beat this record by a couple of months, achieving the title at the age of 15.

Judit is the youngest of three sisters who are all amongst the best women chess players in the world. Their parents trained the three girls to show that women's achievements in chess can be just as great as men's. Now, many experts tip Judit Polgar as a future World Champion.

Going further

If you would like to become a chess problemist, you could join The British Chess Problem Society. It publishes a magazine, *The Problemist*, six times a year. The British Chess Problem Society is open to people from any country – not just Britain. You can find out more by writing to the address on the right.

The Secretary
The British Chess Problem Society
76 Albany Drive
Herne Bay
Kent CT6 8SJ
ENGLAND

Algebraic notation

Algebraic notation records moves using letters, numbers and symbols. The ranks on the board are numbered and the files are lettered. Each piece is referred to by its initial, except for the Knight, which is N and Pawns, for which no initial is used.

A move is written using the initial of the piece and the grid reference of the square it moves to. For example, **Nh3** means the Knight moves to square h3, and **Be3** means the Bishop moves to e3. When a Pawn moves, only the grid reference of its new position is given. For example, **f4** means that a Pawn moves to f4.

Sometimes it is not clear which piece moves so in this case both the initial and file letter of the piece are given. For example, the move **Ne6** could be made by either of the Knights on the board on the right. **Nce6** indicates that the move is made by the Knight on the c-file.

The moves are numbered and White's move is always written first. If Black's move is written without White's, dots are printed after the move number, for example, **4...Ng6**.

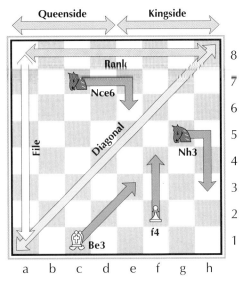

Symbols used in notation

Symbol	Example	
x	Bxh8	Bishop captures the piece on h8. (When a Pawn captures, only its file letter is given. For example, **bxc5** means that the Pawn on the b-file captures the piece on square c5.)
+	Re7+	Rook moves to e7 and puts the King in check.
++	Re7++	Rook moves to e7 and checkmates the King.
0-0		Castles Kingside (files e-h).
0-0-0		Castles Queenside (files a-d).
(Q)	a8(Q)	White Pawn reaches the eighth rank and is promoted to a Queen.
(N)	d1(N)	Black Pawn promotes to a Knight.